CONTENTS

Introduction

Having been in the nursing profession for more than forty years I have seen some changes - some for the better, others not so. I decided to write this record of my career covering the first twenty-five years. I have included some of my more memorable experiences; such things are unlikely to happen again in these modern days of nursing. Now I teach staff and, apart from the odd assessment visit, I rarely see patients. I am quite pleased about that, as time seems to be in short supply as are all of the other resources (including staff). Most of the trained nursing staff's time is spent on endless paperwork, leaving the human side of actual nursing care to the much-exploited nursing assistants.

When I meet with my old colleagues (from my training days) we despair at the fall in standards and agree that we had the best of it. Unlike our predecessors, we were allowed to get married and continue working; a little make up was permitted and we never worked split shifts or more than a twelve hour shift.

We were, moreover, taught to be polite to all - including relatives - and would never take anything to a patient's bedside without it being either on a tray or a trolley. Hair had to be pinned above collar length and woe betide the nurse who was caught sitting on a patient's bed!

Sister (not the ward or unit manager as they are known these days) was to be respected, as was Matron.

Those of us oldies still working today went back to university to convert our old SRN qualification to the degree course and/or speciality in order to stay in the profession; but I am still grateful for the high standard of my training days and I hope that you will enjoy reading about my career.

This book spans a period between the 'ladies with the lamp' lightly treading the old Nightingale wards and the high-tech machine watchers in a modern Intensive care unit, to bring you a true taste of how nursing could be in the 1970's up to the late 1980's.

All of the stories are true, but names and places have been changed in order to maintain patient confidentiality, and to fill any shortfall in my memory. The first of these stories, 'A Hard Night at St. Cuthbert's', was published in my second book of short stories, 'The Dark Lantern', but its rightful place is in this volume with all of the other tales from my early nursing days.

Happy reading.

Lyn Watts – East Sussex March 2018

A Hard Night at St Cuthbert's

Sally Bryant yawned and stretched, then drained the dregs of her coffee. She stuck her knitting needles through her wool and stuffed the part knitted baby jacket into her knitting bag with the other coloured balls of wool. Sally was a staff nurse at St Cuthbert's hospital, one of the oldest hospitals in London. Built in the 1300's by monks to serve the poor sick of the city, it was an ancient building with numerous corridors, nooks and crannies.

Usually on day duty on the Coronary Ward, Sally had been asked to swap onto nights for the week due to staff sickness. She was a little nervous in the old building at night. It was set around a square courtyard and all of the outer doors were locked at night obliging the staff to travel from wing to wing via the basement corridors. These were ancient, musty and the only lights were the dim night lights casting a greenish hue giving the impression of being in a semi-dark cave.

To get from the Coronary wing to the staff canteen for her meal break Sally had to travel from one side of the square to the other via that basement corridor. Going to break wasn't too bad but coming back was eerie. Once in the canteen, the junior doctors used to entertain the nurses with stories and legends of the ancient hospital. It broke the boredom of reheated, microwaved, meals and tasteless coffee from the machine. Sally joined her friend, Katie (from orthopaedics) to eat their supper together. Soon they were joined by Dr Simon Diamond. He delighted in scaring the nurses and always seemed to have a new sensational story or spooky tale to tell.

Sally had finished eating and was on her second cup of strong black coffee when he started. Noting that Sally was knitting baby clothes for her sister - who was about to deliver her first child - he asked: had they heard the story of the ghostly Sister? "Here we go!" remarked Katie under her breath.

Without waiting for a reply from the girls, Simon began. He told of a Sister Margaret at the hospital during the second war. She had the misfortune to fall truly and deeply in love with a man she had met at a tea dance. They saw each other twice weekly - on her night off and on her half day. They spoke of marriage, but he enlisted as a fighter pilot in the RAF at the outbreak of hostilities. Before he went away they spent the night together. He bought her a modest ring and wrote to her regularly from his base in Kent.

The inevitable happened; his plane was hit by ground fire on his way back from a mission, he limped back to base but had to crash land. He was quite severely burnt before the ground crew could get him out of the cockpit. He was brought into St

2

Cuthbert's and, strangely, to the very ward of his sweetheart. She nursed him most diligently, but he was morose and reluctant to talk to her. She put this down to shock and the pain from his injuries, but, after a couple of days, he had visitors. A tall slim woman arrived to see him accompanied by a child of about four or five years. On being asked her identity she announced herself to be his wife and the little girl his daughter!

Margaret gave no outward sign of shock or surprise at all; she showed the woman to his bedside and left them to it. After the visitors had left Margaret was doing the drug round before lights out and the patients settled for the night. She took her paramour his pain killers and sleeping pills. She had increased the dose ten times! On her second hourly ward round she found him stiff and cold with blue lips. Calmly pulling the sheets over his face, she opened the window. They were three floors up. She jumped to her death on the square below.

"They do say" continued Simon "that her poor shade stalks the corridors at night as a dark shadow, following other nurses to warn them against the same mistake, her penance for her guilt at what she had done!"

"Poppycock!" said Katie. Then, looking anxiously at her watch; "Gosh! Time I went back."

"Me too!" said Sally, and, picking up her bag, she set off for her lonely walk under the square along the dark corridors to get back to the coronary wing. Her mind was filled with the tragic story of poor Sister Margaret. She had heard rumours of a suicide during the war years. Her ears detected a faint sound: 'Splat, swish-swish, rattle -rattle splat swish-swish!'

The hairs on the back of her neck rose. She became acutely aware of the shadows. Looking around she saw a dark shadowy blob bouncing along the corridor behind her. She felt her mouth dry up and her blood freeze. Quickening her pace, the blob quickened too. She could see the light at the end of the tunnel by the lifts. She started running. The blob kept up with her pace, bouncing crazily along behind her, at the same time the splat swishy noise grew louder, feeling as though her heart would burst she ran headlong towards the light then smack!

She ran straight into old Phil, the night porter, who was mopping the floor with soapy water. Splat, the mop went; then swish-swish and finally rattle-rattle in the metal bucket before the next splat!

" 'ere, 'ere steady on nurse." he said

"Oh! Phil! Thank God!" she began; but he cut her short.

"Look 'ere, Staff," he said, "your ball of wool is trailing

along behind you! Caught on your knitting bag! Good job
it didn't unravel itself!"

Sister in Training

I was fortunate to train at one of London's most prestigious hospitals. St. Cuthbert's, or Bert's as it was affectionately known, was built in the 12th Century to care for the sick poor of London. Originally a monastery, it still had some of the old buildings incorporated into it.

My nurse training commenced at the beginning of the 1970's, when the wards were still the long 'nightingale' wards and nurses still wore striped dresses with starched collars, caps, and aprons. Pay was poor, but we were looked after very well. During our first year there was a curfew on coming in at night and men were not, under any circumstances, allowed into the nurses' living quarters.

We were always hungry and spent many a meal break trying to decide what would make us feel the most full for the least money. Many a lunchbreak was spent deciding whether to have coffee after our lunch, or spend the last five minutes of our break dashing to the hospital shop to buy a fresh pair of black tights as there was a ladder in the ones we were wearing!

Discipline was strict both on the wards and in our classrooms but our tutors were fair and kind to us. We always felt supported. Recently my old tutor described us as: "Sometimes timid, but always well-disciplined young ladies." I think that summed it up rather well.

This, then, was the scene, our working and living conditions for the duration of our training, and, for some of us, beyond. Work was hard and very often emotionally draining. For many of us, it was our first time away from home and most of us were just eighteen years old.

Naturally those who work hard tend to play hard. Bert's had its own social club and there were several city pubs within a stone's throw of the hospital. These were always full of Bert's doctors and nurses. Our social lives were as full as our working hours. Somehow we still found some time to study for our nursing exams.

The first ten weeks or so were spent in classroom-based theoretical learning. Then we were allowed onto our first ward. During the first two weeks of our ward placements there was an accident opposite the hospital as two of our students were returning to the hospital from lunch. An elderly lady had fallen whilst getting off a bus. A small knot of people had gathered around her. Violet, one of our set, elbowed her way through the crowd saying "Move! Please, let me through! Stand back! I am a nurse! Give me space!" she elbowed her way to the front and bent over the lady. "It's alright, dear," she soothed, "I am a nurse you will be okay!" "I know she will." said a voice. Then, sounding a little peeved, "I am a doctor and I have already examined her!" Vi looked up to see one of our most senior Accident and Emergency consultants looking down at her. It was definitely one of those red faced moments!

The world was a frightening place during those days. In the early 1970's we suffered the IRA bombing campaign on London. St Cuthbert's was next door to one of London's most famous legal landmarks. Sadly that was a target for a terrorist bomb while I was still a student nurse. It was a steep learning curve. We were dealing with people with horrific injuries - some of them still wearing their lawyer's wigs and gowns. It was my first experience of the amazing 'all get stuck in together' mentality that made Bert's the brilliant hospital it was. I had been about to go off duty when the bomb exploded. Walking across the square I felt the ground shake under my feet and my ears rang with the blast - in fact they didn't stop hissing for hours afterwards.

Seeing the smoke I thought there had been an explosion in one of our laboratories so I ran across the square towards them. However, I was soon diverted by the sight of the first of the walking wounded as they came towards me. Many were still in their legal finery, clutching handkerchiefs to foreheads covered

8

with bloodstained wigs. Every spare staff member gravitated towards the A. and E. department. We were kept frantically busy there for the next several hours.

No one complained. Nor did we expect any overtime pay; however, we looked after each other by sending everyone off (singly) for a half hour break to rest and eat when we were able to spare someone. I do not recall ever being charged for the soup, sandwiches and coffee which seemed to arrive in an endless stream from the canteen.

Night duty was something quite different. The shift started at 9.15pm with handover/report from the day staff. There was always something to do but, in the early hours, if all was quiet, one could sit at the desk at the head of the ward where the rows of patient's beds could clearly be seen. By the subdued light of the desk lamp we students could catch up on our study of human anatomy and physiology.

During my final year of training the Tower of London fell victim to an IRA bomb. Bert's took some of the casualties. Amongst them were a honeymoon couple from Scandinavia. Their injuries were bad, but not life threatening. We all felt so sorry for them that matron found a side room and ordered an extra bed to be put in it for them. There they spent the rest of their honeymoon side by side in twin hospital beds. They became very popular with the staff and really made the best of their misfortune, showing amazing spirit and resilience.

I was working with one of my closest friends on the Cardiac ward when we got our final results. Unbelievably, the day had come at last when we could both sport a navy blue petersham belt with a shiny silver buckle. Finally we were staff nurses.

I spent six months working as staff nurse on a male surgical ward. During this time I earnt the nickname 'Liquorice Legs' from the patients due to the thick sixty-denier black tights we all wore. By now I was living out of hospital quarters and riding a moped to work each day, so these kept my legs warm on cold mornings whilst riding in. I remember a crusty old man on this ward. He was an ex RAF man who was extremely rude to and demanding of all of us nurses. I was quite fond of him as he made me laugh. He would demand tea or the paper then, when it was brought to him, he would tell us to: "Go and jump in the Thames!" I believe it was just his sense of humour, but one day sister heard him demand tea. "Please, Mr Meakins, you must say please to my girls!" she berated him, waving a finger under his nose. He didn't say a word but as she walked away up the ward I heard him mutter under his breath: "Damned old Mrs Please!" She was 'Damned old Mrs Please' to him from that moment onwards. After my six months there I decided that my love of surgery was so great that I applied for, and got, the staff nurse job. I then began working in the operating theatres.

Theatres quickly became a place where I could take pride in my work. It could be stressful - especially duty theatre, where the emergency cases were taken for life saving surgery. But we played hard too. The sinks where we 'scrubbed up' for surgery were long metal troughs. The theatre porters thought it great sport to fill these with water at the end of an operating list whilst we were cleaning the theatre suite. If you weren't concentrating they would pick you up bodily and throw you into said trough! We all wore theatre kit which was about to be sent to the laundry, so that wasn't a major problem but our underwear would get soaked through.

This happened to me so often that I kept a spare set of undies in my locker. I would put my wet set into the heated lotions cabinet to dry. One of the porters, Andy, thought it the height of wit to run around the place with my bra on his head shouting: "Where do I come from? Edinbra!"

The theatre I 'staffed' on had a sister in charge with whom I got on very well. Working together was a real pleasure. The only fly in our ointment was a registrar surgeon who was a real chauvinist. He would smack our bottoms and demand we made his tea for him. He would make sexist remarks and occasionally have wandering hands. After one particularly trying shift we decided to get our revenge on him. At the end of the list he would go into the shower demanding we bring him a towel. This particular day we pretended to leave his towel outside the cubicle for him but instead, took all his clothes away. We thought he would have to get into a fresh theatre strip while all wet and go searching for his clothes. How wrong we were.

He bellowed to us to bring his clothes back at once, we answered this with a volley of giggles and laughter. "I'm warning you!" he bellowed; more laughter from us. What we had overlooked were his shoes and socks. They were still in the changing room. While we were chortling with glee at our ingenuity, he appeared wearing his shoes and only one sock placed rather strategically. We squealed and ran away into the ladies changing room throwing his clothes at him as we fled. None of us ever mentioned it again, but his behaviour did improve a little after that.

After a few months of happily working together, sister was signed off on long-term sick leave. I was asked to act up in her absence. Our late shift started at 1pm. I was living in a flat just a few miles from Bert's. Preparing for late shift one day I was enjoying a second cup of coffee when the morning news interrupted my thoughts. There had been an horrendous train crash at Moorgate, one of the underground stations fairly close to Bert's. I knew we would be on-call for the casualties. Immediately I shelved the coffee, grabbed my coat and headed to the hospital. I wouldn't see my flat again for forty eight hours.

As I turned the corner of the road to Bert's I saw queues of Londoners waiting to donate blood. Almost every staff member had arrived to help whether or not they were supposed to be on duty. Our theatre took casualty after casualty. We were taking it in turns to go and sleep in the coffee lounge for a couple of hours at a time. The scouts were going up and down the theatre blocks and A. and E., keeping the tea and coffee supplies topped up and, again, bringing an endless supply of soup and sandwiches to keep our strength up.

We would sleep for an hour or two at most then eat and ..er in the changing rooms. We would don fresh theatre strip and dive straight back into the fray.

We witnessed some horrific injuries and there were some desperately sad cases. A lot of people didn't survive. Many perished in the underground tunnel where the train had crashed. Some of our very young, brave junior doctors were heroes that day. They went down into the wreckage to do whatever they could for the injured and dying.

It seemed a very long time before, finally, the flow of casualties became a mere trickle and I was sent off duty. I found that I could not simply go home. I felt hollow inside yet I did not want to be alone, I gravitated to the hospital social club.

Most of us on duty that day had had the same idea. The room was quite full but untypically silent. Usually there would be loud juke box music playing, glasses tinkling and chatter and banter similar to the parrot house at London Zoo as everyone let off steam. Tonight you could hear a pin drop. A low murmur could be heard. It was the only sound. There was no music. People were sitting staring at their drinks with a faraway look in their eyes. We had seen hell and had no desire to talk about it; and yet we needed to be together, in each other's company.

When I finally left to go home the only sound in the nurse's locker rooms was of gentle sobbing. It is not an event I like to reflect on, even after the passage of over forty years.

I arrived for my regular shift on theatre the following day. We weren't operating until the afternoon so the morning would be spent sterilizing the instruments and laying up the trollies. My colleague and friend, Samantha, was working with me. She went into the sluice and I heard a muffled squeal. I dashed in to see if she was okay and she was standing there, eyes like saucers, pointing to the sluice worktop. On it was a latex surgeon's glove filled with what must have been at least a gallon of water and knotted at the wrist. The fingers stuck up giving it a bloated, cow's udder appearance. After the first shock we started giggling – it was just what we needed. "What shall we do with it?" asked Sam. We decided to lift it between us and dump it in the deep sluice sink where we could pop it to drain it off.

It is a lesser known law of physics, that when two women start lifting something either heavy or awkward! It renders them incapable of normal behaviour and everything becomes hysterically funny! We tried to lift the udder. It slithered and shook and spidged out of our fingers. By the fourth attempt we were both crying with laughter and could hardly stagger along with the thing. We had just got it poised over the sink when Andy jumped around the door of the sluice and pushed us both together, causing it to burst all over us!

We all laughed so much it was worth the unexpected change of clothes and underwear, which we dried, as usual, in the heated lotions cabinet. It was just what we needed after the previous few days of horror. I didn't even mind seeing Andy running around the anaesthetic room with my bra on his head! How I loved my mad colleagues at Bert's!

Sister on Nights

The porters at Bert's loved to try and scare us nurses at night. The hospital had been founded in the twelfth century by a monk called Brother Caleb following a dream he had had in which St Cuthbert appeared to him instructing him to build a hospital for the sick poor of London.

Caleb had suffered with chest complaints and a persistent cough. His dream occurred during one particularly bad spell of illness from which he had recovered. Building St Cuthbert's was his way of giving thanks for his deliverance from his sickbed.

Rumour had it that his ghost still walked the old part of the hospital. He was reported to be visible only from the knees up since the floor had been raised up some decades previously and Caleb walked on the old floor level. One or two of the night porters and nurses (since retired), had claimed to have seen his ghost accompanied by his heavy asthmatic breathing. The porters loved to regale us with scary tales of his wanderings at night.

Now it just so happened that during my time as a student nurse I spent an eight week placement on the children's ward located in the oldest part of Bert's. The duty rota gave me a week of night duty during this period which meant working from 9pm until 7.30 the next morning. I won't go into details about the sadness of caring for sick children. Many of them were terminally ill and died of various cancers and other nasties (most of which are, happily, treatable these days). Suffice it to say it was a very tiring and emotional eight weeks, not least when your body is worn down by lack of sleep as I never could manage to sleep more than three or four hours during the day.

It was on one of these nights that I went into the sluice to stock up, tidy and polish the bedpans. It was deathly quiet in the old part of the building at night, especially in the sluice, which was at the furthest end of the ward away from the nurse's station where my colleague sat. I worked by a very dim night light and was lost in thought when I suddenly heard a rasping sound, a bit like a drawn out breath. I paused and listened...... Silence!

I continued my work and "Raaassppp" there it was again, and, once more, the hairs on the back of my neck stood up and I felt myself go pale. Just as I was feeling cold and flaky, I saw something move out of the corner of my eye. It was between me and the door or else I would have fled. My heart pounded. "Raaaassssppp, Raaassssppp", I looked down. There on the floor, slowly crawling towards the drain was an enormous cockroach - one of the many that infested the old building and came out at night to drink. Stuck to its foot was a sweet wrapper. It was this which was making the rasping sound as it dragged across the old stone floor.

Sick children sometimes have strange eating habits and Sister always let them eat whatever they fancied; the theory being that any food is better than no food at all. Needless to say sweeties were always popular, but, not with this poor cockroach who dragged the penny chew wrapper around like shackles. Summoning almost superhuman courage I stood on the edge of the chew wrapper and the cockroach freed its foot, scuttling off under the sink. I finished up quickly and left the sluice and my erstwhile friend as soon as I could. It took me some time to stop trembling and I found myself a little more jumpy than usual when my colleague went off on her break.

On occasions Bert's junior doctors rugby team would take on the rugby team from another famous London hospital, Guy's. There was precious little love lost between them and, on some occasions, sportsmanship would turn into brawling in the hospital's social club bar.

It was following such a night that Charlie, the barman, opened up about 10.30 one morning to prepare for the lunchtime sandwich trade. To his horror, he was greeted with two Guy's junior doctors sitting on the floor back to back each side of a barstool. I was working in the fracture clinic that day and he came rushing over, breathless and grinning with eyes like saucers. "Quick, Staff, lend me the plaster cutters pronto!" He gasped.

It appears that, following defeat, some of the Bert's medical students and junior doctors from the rugby team had invited their vanquishers, the Guy's team, back to the hospital bar for a drink. Rather a lot of alcohol had been consumed and the Guy's team were bragging about their victory and ribbing the Bert's lads over their defeat.

They weren't in the mood to stop drinking when Charlie left at 11.15. One of the more sensible (or so Charlie thought) 3rd year students pushed a £20 note across the bar and promised that when the kitty ran out they would lock up and leave. Bert's men were known for their honesty and integrity, so Charlie agreed and went off to catch his night bus home. When he arrived the following morning, the two Guy's medical students had been plastered together, back to back each side of the bar stool with plaster of Paris which had hardened by the time they awoke from their drunken stupor. Thus, they were forced to spend the night in the bar plastered in more ways than one! Of course no one owned up to it or admitted knowing anything about it. The Guy's men couldn't remember how it had happened so no more was said; but Charlie never trusted them to lock up again!

Now I finished my nurse training working on the cardiac ward, which was on the third floor of the modern building across the road from the older part of the hospital. Open heart surgery was still in its infancy and some patient's, sadly, didn't survive the operations. We experienced the deaths of quite a few young patients, but there were some wonderful successes too. One patient, Mr Fuller, stays in my mind as he was about six feet four inches tall. He was being cared for on this particular day by Rose, a small Scottish nurse of about five feet two.

The patients were allowed to wander up and down the ward to stretch their legs if they were deemed fit enough. Sometimes they would wander off to the lifts outside the ward to see their visitors off after visiting time or to greet them on arrival. Bert's always stored the hospital wheelchairs in the area by the lifts outside the wards.

On the day in question, Mr Fuller had wandered off towards the lifts when Rose wanted to give him his medication. She hurried after him and overtook him by the lifts next to the wheelchairs. "Will you come back with me please, Mr Fuller." she scolded; at which point he turned towards Rose with a purple face, clutched his chest and pitched forward onto her. She grabbed him and managed to spin him round by about forty five degrees then pushed him back, and into, a waiting wheelchair. Her legs straddled his knees, her dress had risen up her thighs and her hat was skewed at a jaunty angle where he had knocked it as he had landed on her. With hair awry and very red in the face, little Rose realised that Mr Fuller had died. At the very second of realisation the lift sounded 'ting' and the doors opened to reveal the first batch of evening visitors, who were suitably open-mouthed to witness a nurse in a typical 'Carry on' film position!

Fortunately none of them were for Mr Fuller but, so as not to alarm them, Rose grabbed the shoulders of his dressing gown and held Mr Fuller's lifeless body firmly upright in the chair as she smartly wheeled him back to his bed and the privacy of the curtains with a loud "Come on, Mr Fuller, back to bed with you, now!" for the benefit of the unsuspecting visitors. Poor Rose, but how well she coped!

Sister in trouble

My time in theatre at St Cuthbert's was very interesting and I loved it. All sorts of funny things happened. I had only been a staff nurse on orthopaedic theatre for a few months when my friend, Sarah, the theatre sister, was obliged to go on long-term sick leave and I had to act up as sister in her absence.

We were a very close-knit team. Most of us were young – I was a twenty three year old, shapely, redhead at that time. The registrar surgeons were only eight or nine years older in most cases, and all of us were still learning by experience.

At that time we sterilized all the instruments ourselves in the two large autoclave machines which were kept in the 'sterile room' adjoining the operating room. Whilst I did often 'scrub up' and assist the surgeon, my main love was anaesthetics. Later this led me to work on resuscitation teams and kick-started my career as a resuscitation officer and, later, as a trainer; but that is another story.

One day I was not assisting the surgeon. There was a theatre technician assisting the anaesthetist, so I was in the sterile room, sterilizing the instruments and laying up the trolleys for the rest of the day's operations. In order to do this I had to be scrubbed and wear a sterile gown. That particular day was one featuring many total hip replacements. These operations took a great number of instruments and most of them were heavy. There were drills, saws, reamers, chisels, mallets and a selection of different sized metal templates for heads of femur and acetabular cups. All of these were on heavy metal trays and, on being taken from the autoclave, they were put onto a shelf which was covered with a sterile green cloth. The instruments were then laid up onto sterile trolleys in order of use ready for each operation in turn, all of which were covered with another sterile green cloth.

Earlier that morning - this was an afternoon list - the maintenance men had been servicing the autoclaves. They had been obliged to remove the big instrument shelf in order to take the side panel off. Unbeknown to me, they had accidentally forgotten to affix the screws onto the side brackets when they replaced said shelf. This meant that only the middle bracket had screws in it. John was the registrar operating that day and he was a close friend of mine. He subsequently became one of the country's leading orthopaedic surgeons, but this was his early days and he was still quite 'green'. Silence reigned in the operating room as he worked; and I worked quietly in the open bay next door (which was the sterile room). We could see each other if we chose to do so.

We wore anti-static wooden clogs in theatre. The long green sterile gown I was wearing was made for a much taller person than myself and so came down past my ankles. I was gloved and masked-up as I took the latest tray of hot sterile instruments from the autoclave. I placed it onto the shelf which was, in turn, covered with a sterile green cloth. As I did so the mallet, undoubtedly the heaviest instrument on the tray, slid to one side. This unbalanced the weight ratio and, since the shelf was only held on by its central screw, the whole thing turned upside down dashing the instrument tray to the ground with a clatter reminiscent of an explosion in a cutlery factory! So as to avoid having red hot instruments falling on my legs and feet I instinctively jumped back. I fell out of my clog and tripped on the long gown I was wearing before unceremoniously falling backwards onto my bottom! When the clanging and clunking of the metallic catastrophe had died away, I became aware of total shocked silence; except for one of the round acetabular cup templates which rolled into the operating room with a low rumbling noise. It rolled round and round the operating table with a noise increasing in pitch and speed then came to rest right at John's feet. The ridiculousness of the situation struck me and I started to giggle! I then burst into hysterical laughter - shoulders shaking and rocking back and forth on the floor. "Oh my God, Lyn!" shouted John; then, dropping his instruments onto the scrubbed nurses' sterile trolley, he rushed into the sterile room and scooped me up in his arms. (He was six foot three inches and a rugby player!) "Are you okay? What happened? Say something!" He implored me while carrying me through to the coffee room where he could place me on a chair. Eventually I could gasp sufficiently to indicate that I was fine, other than a twisted ankle. Once I had regained my composure I pointed out to him that we were now both unsterile and would need to scrub up again. It was a rather red-faced John who walked back into the operating room to resume the procedure. As he did so I rang the maintenance department and read them the riot act. I had to start again with sterilising the instruments. The anaesthetist, and assisting house-officer, were staring open mouthed! I should add that the operation was successful and the patient did very well post operatively too.

I mentioned that we were a close team. We looked out for each other, but that didn't mean that we were above playing a few practical jokes. We had a new theatre porter working on the theatre block for the first time. His name was Jeffery and, at first, he got a few backs up by adopting a rather superior air. He let it be known that this was only a 'stop-gap' job until he could find something better - even though it quickly became common knowledge that he had been out of work for months prior to starting with us.

He tried to make us all feel small by bragging of his scientific knowledge and of how he would have gone to medical school if he hadn't fallen on hard times and needed to work. One day we had had enough. We hatched a plan.

One of the procedures carried out in the vascular theatre was called a trouser graft. When the main aorta has an aneurysm, the distended portion can be removed and replaced with a stent. If this is at the point where the aorta divides into the two main leg arteries, the stent is shaped like a tiny pair of trousers, hence the name trouser graft for the procedure. That day we asked Jeffrey to go and get the trouser graft machine from theatre A at basement level and bring up to our theatre. No such machine existed outside of our fevered imaginations, of course. Once he had set off on his errand we rang theatre A to appraise them of the situation. When Jeffery arrived, they duly sent him up to theatre B to be informed there that it had just been sent up to theatre D. They then rang theatre D to warn them and prepared them to ring theatre E, and so on until he had gone up to the top theatre F, where he was told it had already been sent back down to us!

On another occasion we sent him to the pharmacy to collect a bottle of intravenous oxygen! My own brainwave was very simple really! I sent him to the theatre curators for a packet of fallopian tubes! He came down from his high horse after a few of these pranks and finally became a valued member of the team.

Eventually, after spending time as a district nurse and a practice nurse, I took a course in anaesthetic nursing and, following my move to Sussex, spent some time as an anaesthetic nurse in a small private hospital. If there was an emergency on any of the wards I was summoned to lead the medical emergency/resuscitation team. The anaesthetist, quite rightly, could not leave his anaesthetised patient. From that beginning I began training the staff in resuscitation and life support, before returning back to the NHS as a Resuscitation Officer. There I was responsible for staff training programmes, life support equipment plus logging and auditing any cardiac arrests which occurred. I specialised in life support and the NHS funded my teacher training.

I never returned to hands-on nursing, but I keep up my RGN registration to give credibility to my work, and just in case......

Sister through the changes

After some happy years I moved to East Sussex with my family, so left behind my beloved Bert's. Initially I had the best of both worlds; I worked two mornings a week in the theatre at the small cottage hospital in the town, and three mornings a week on the community as a district nurse.

Eventually, I took a promotion and gave up the hospital altogether. I was then working five mornings and alternate weekends on the community; but, at the beginning of my time in the county I had some strange and amusing experiences on theatre.

The orthopaedic surgeon I worked with on Tuesday and Thursday mornings was a round, very overweight, jolly man who, to me, looked as I imagined the emperor Nero must have looked. He was short but fat and had a shock of iron grey hair, in addition to a twinkle in his blue eyes and an overdeveloped sense of humour. Eric Reynolds always called me 'Legs' short for 'Leggy Lyn' and we got on famously. We would banter the whole time, but he was extremely kind and much loved by his patients.

Now Eric, although only in his mid-fifties had such a weight problem that he was booked into a private hospital to have both hips replaced. This meant that movement was painful for him and bending down to change his surgeon's boots for his shoes and vice-versa was nigh on impossible. Being a consultant specialist (and a proud man), he didn't want the younger staff nurses or the auxiliary nurses helping him. He would only allow myself, or my friend, Steph, who was the hospital matron, to help him.

In those days, before the brand new hospital was built at the bottom of the town, the old cottage hospital was quite primitive. There was only one changing room which was shared by the male doctors as well as us nursing staff. We managed very well though, for if one was in there changing into theatre strip, one simply closed the door. Everyone knew then to wait until the door opened again before entering.

Outside in the corridor was the fridge with a kettle and tea and coffee making facilities on it where the auxiliaries made tea or coffee for everyone at the end of the operating session. The changing room looked directly onto this when the door was open.

This particular day, Eric had finished operating and was changing while we cleared up and whilst coffee was being made. He called me in to the changing room once he was decent to help him on with his shoes and tie the laces for him. Now we had a fairly new auxiliary nurse called Louise, who was very shy and seemed terrified of all the surgeons. Today I was kneeling down between Eric's ample thighs tying his shoelaces with my head down and the door open out of a sense of propriety. Louise came round the corner to make the coffee, took one look at my back, with my head between Eric's thighs. She gasped, clapped her hand over her mouth and then ran away into the office. "Crickey Legs! That's torn it!" Muttered Eric. I sighed: "Oh God! Leave her to me." And, finishing, I stood up and wandered off after her.

I found her in the office, pretending to read the patient kardex. She was bright red in the face and trembling. I put a conciliatory arm around her shoulders and said "Now Louise, you will find that sometimes the doctors ask you to carry out certain little personal services for them…." At this point she gasped again, her eyes were like saucers but before she could speak I continued: "Like doing up their shoelaces when their hips are too painful to allow bending!"

She looked as though she had been sandbagged. Her expression was priceless and I watched wave after wave of conflicting emotion cross her face (which was reddening by the second). Smiling I asked "Well what did YOU think we were doing?" Not waiting for her flustered reply I swept out, leaving her to scuttle off and make the coffee whilst I wrote up the operations book; another rewarding day at the office.

Eric often used to get important phone calls while he was operating. This involved us running back and forth with messages and answers to the person on the other end of the phone. One day I was not scrubbed for the surgery as I was manning the paperwork and phones in the office. I took a call from his house officer up at the county hospital. He needed some test results for a patient as a matter of urgency. I went into Eric in theatre. "Blimey, Legs!" he exclaimed, "They are in my briefcase in the changing room, can you get them out and tell him over the phone, the key to my case is in my breast pocket." I walked back to the phone and promised to ring back directly with the results once I had found them. I then went back into theatre. The scrub team wore sterile green gowns over their theatre strip when actually operating. In order to get to Eric's pocket for the key I had to stand behind him, where his back was unsterile, put my arms around him under his green gown and slide my hands into his breast pocket. This I did but found no key. "Oh! Wait, Legs," he said "I think it is in my left trouser pocket."

Much to the amusement of the house officer assisting him I slid my hand down into his deep trouser pocket, no key!, I tried the right trouser pocket with no luck, then, at his suggestion I tried both back trouser pockets in turn to no avail. I couldn't see past his ample back but I could hear the hoots of laughter coming from the op team, as (unbeknown to me at the time) he pulled all sorts of comical mock-ecstatic faces. Finally when I told him we had drawn a blank he pretended to remember that the key was hanging up in his jacket pocket in the changing room! Red faced I retrieved it, found the results and rang them through - typical of his humour.

There was a celebrity living within five miles of the cottage hospital - a superstar, famous for playing in a glam rock band. Reggie Sultry was a hard drinking, hard living, fabulously wealthy star who made his millions from his song writing and guitar playing. All the more concerning, then, when he broke his hand while smashing up the furniture in his mansion in a drunken rage after a party.

Eric had operated on him as a private patient and had prescribed very strong painkilling suppositories for him to take at home for a few days following his surgery. We wondered if they would make any difference to him as his body was probably immune to drugs due to his hellraising lifestyle. Over coffee in the office one day after the op list, I took a phone call from him asking for Eric. Passing him the phone, I watched his face changing from puzzlement to delight. He struggled to contain his mirth.

The conversation had gone something like this: Reggie- "Ere Doc, do I 'ave to keep taking these bloody things, only I'm running out of parking space!" Eric: "How come? You are only supposed to be taking a maximum of three over twenty-four hours!" Reggie: "Oh! (A pause. Then:) Well it says on the bloody box eight hourly!" Eric hung up. His shoulders shook with laughter and for some moments he couldn't speak as he was laughing so much. Finally he sighed, wiping the tears of laughter from his eyes with the back of his hands. He said to me "God, Legs, the thought of Reggie shoving eight of those things up his arse every hour!" This produced fresh bouts of laughter from us both. Life could be great in the cottage at times!

Sister in the Country

The forest was vast and beautiful. A wonderful place to ride horses or walk dogs, but to find my patients - well that was a huge challenge. I had moved from my teaching hospital in London to East Sussex with my husband and our young daughter. I was born in Kent, not far from Sussex and whilst enjoying my work in the big London hospital, I had desperately missed the countryside and the country folk.

We lived in a small village, near a market town on the edges of the lovely Ashdown Forest. I rode my horse in the forest and worked part time as a district nurse driving around numerous rural villages and parts of the market town. The forest was dotted with small enclaves of cottages and some quiet rural houses, which were difficult to find. Today I was visiting two elderly brothers - sheep farmers on the forest who were becoming incapacitated with age and arthritis but still kept their sheep and their cheerful dispositions.

The only problem was that these foresters had such broad Sussex accents and only about three teeth between them, making them very difficult to understand not least because every two or three words they said would be punctuated with either

'Ooo' or 'Ahh' followed by raucous laughter. This earnt them the name of 'The Ooo Ahhs' amongst us nurses.

I had visited them that morning to give Jonas his Iron injection and to check that Eli was managing his diabetes properly. I finished work at 1pm and my daughter didn't finish school until 3.30 so I tried whenever possible to ride on the forest for an hour or so if the weather was halfway decent.

That afternoon I was riding with a friend, Jenny, and her horse Bert. He was a rescue case and had been abused in the past so he could be a bit strong and stroppy. He lacked a front tooth giving him a slightly comical bandito like appearance. He and Jenny had a love / hate relationship, she loved him but he played her up more than a little. This afternoon he had decided to take fright at an imaginary monster in the undergrowth and pitching her off with a buck like a trebuchet, he thundered off in the general direction of the forest tearooms.

I pointed my mare towards his retreating rear end and gave chase (having first established that Jenny was not injured). The sound of Jenny screaming profanities at Bert, was ringing in my ears as I galloped after him.

Now the couple who ran the tearooms were patients of mine, or rather the husband was. They had come down from London and bought a plant nursery which they soon turned into a tearoom. Whilst it was a welcome addition to the forest and was popular with walkers, it was somewhat fussy - all paper doilies and little ill-suited serviettes, with lots of floral teacups and tablecloths. Mrs Saunders was a highly strung nervy woman, who made it plain that dogs were only welcome in the garden under sufferance and disapproved of the forest sheep straying too close to the tea garden.

Imagine, then, my horror on rounding the bend to find Bert, reins dragging and stirrups flapping, dancing all over Mrs Saunders precious lawns being fed scones and chocolate sponge-cake by a table of elderly ladies. I jumped off my mare and tied her to the fence before I went to rescue Bert. Apologising to the ladies, who seemed enamoured of Bert's charms, I grabbed his reins as Mrs Saunders rounded on me. "Sister, is he anything to do with you?" At that point Jenny, bleeding from the knee and covered in mud came running around the corner like a banshee screaming curses at Bert and yelling threats like 'burgers' and 'glue factory'.

One of the rather autocratic elderly ladies pitched in to Jenny with: "Don't you dare harm that poor animal!" Mrs Saunders also launched into Jenny bewailing the state of her garden. My mare started helping herself to the cakes on the nearest table on the other side of the fence where she was tied, much to the amusement of the children with that party who squealed and giggled with delight. I was trying to pull her away and be heard amidst this cacophony when I caught sight of two familiar, bent, figures loading a sheep into their old pick-up truck. They were on the other side of the forest road opposite the tea rooms. The Ooo Ahhs! Just what I needed at that particular moment, I thought. Then: "Coooeee, Sister!" followed by much merriment, mirthful laughter and a lot of unintelligible words (which I am afraid I just smiled and nodded at!)

By that time Jenny had soothed Mrs Saunders, bought a huge coffee cake, to be collected later, by way of recompense and remounted for our journey back. The elder brother called out something totally unintelligible to her and the younger one nodded sagely. "Yes indeed." She replied smiling. At this both brothers roared with raucous laughter, their thin shoulders shaking as they looked at the pair of us with great amusement.

"What on earth did I just agree to?" queried Jenny. I had no idea, but I dreaded my next visit to both Mrs Saunders and the Ooo Ahhs.

*****

I remember one time I was covering maternity leave for a colleague who worked on the twilight district nursing shift. This fitted very well with my young family as the shift ran from 7pm until midnight plus I had the company of a nursing assistant. She was there largely for safety reasons but her company was a real bonus; driving around rural areas at night felt safer in twos.

On this particular evening, we received an emergency call-out to an elderly lady with a blocked urinary catheter. Her house was somewhere in the wilds of the forest. Driving on the forest roads at night was something I wasn't used to. It was pitch black, there were no street lights and half of the houses had long drives which were just grassy tracks between the trees with no house names visible at all.

We had driven around for about ten minutes and had had no luck when I became aware of a small red car following us. I sped up, so did the car behind us. I slowed down and so did our pursuer. I mentioned it to Pat, my assistant. She looked back and decided, in the poor visibility, that she could just about make out that the driver looked male.

This caused us a little alarm. After a brief discussion, we decided to head back to the main road and see if we could shake him off. We did that, he stuck with us like glue. We pulled off into a lay-by and stopped. So did he. When he opened his car door we sped off, only to see him gaining on us again in the rear view mirror. "That's it" I said to Pat, "I'm going to stop at the next lay by and face up to him. Bear in mind that this was the early 1980's

38

before mobile phones were common; the forest was lonely and we were scared. "I'll flag down the next passing car if he tries anything." Pat quavered. Just two hundred yards further on was a forest car park. I pulled into it and stopped the car. Heart pounding but, by now, enraged, I got out of the car. He got out but before I could say anything he stuck out his hand "Good evening, Sister, I'm the duty doctor, Dr Grey. Are you trying to find Mrs Elphick's?"

The flood of relief was mixed with me feeling rather foolish. The Doctor had known that the twilight nurses were on their way to Mrs Elphick's. Being on-call from another area, he didn't know the forest either. Spotting our hats and uniforms he thought he would follow us. He was highly amused and somewhat apologetic when we told him we were lost too and that he had made us nervous. After consulting his ordinance survey map, he led and we followed him, eventually finding poor Mrs Elphick. She needed hospital admission as soon as we had sorted out her catheter and made her comfortable. What an introduction to the new doctor, and thank goodness there were two of us.

Sometimes my sense of humour got the better of me. At these times, it was a welcome break from the sad, and sometimes hopeless, feelings one got; those times when all one could do was to make a patient comfortable, to ease their passing and support their relatives.

One particular occasion came when I was due to meet Dr Briton at Mr and Mrs Luxton's house. The Luxton's lived in a large detached house in a very rural backwater. The houses were built as executive homes in the early 1930's and were accessed from the road via small wooden bridges as there was a spring running past them all at the front of their drives.

Mr and Mrs Luxton were both alcoholics and the home was very spartan. Most of their furniture had been sold to fund their drinking habits. The place had not been decorated since the late 1950's and the Luxton's just sat in armchairs on either side of their empty, cold fireplace listening to an ancient radio.

Dr Briton was visiting that day in order to discuss with them the possibility of them going into residential care. He also had to examine Mrs Luxton, so wanted me to meet him there to act as a chaperone. Dr Briton was very old school. He was very tall and upright with a military bearing, a clipped manner of speaking and a small moustache. I pulled my ancient Morris in behind his Rover in the lane outside the Luxton's house. He was already inside.

He greeted me with a "What, What, Sister, nice of you to join us!" And he glared at his watch. I was two minutes late. He completed his conversation about their future residence and examined Mrs Luxton. He Shuffled all of his things back into his briefcase while I settled her back into her chair. We left the house together discussing their future as we walked back to our respective cars.

Dr Briton was monosyllabic in speech, and had a cut glass accent. He strode out across the wooden bridge with great gangling strides swinging his briefcase back and forth in an exaggerated manner. It had rained that morning and the wood was damp. Green moss grew over it since the Luxton's had few visitors and didn't maintain the property at all.

Suddenly his feet slipped from under him. He managed a frantic jig (worthy of a Cossack dancer!) Time seemed to stand still. His feet went back and forth back and forth. I held my breath then - up went his briefcase and down went Dr Briton onto his bottom on the bridge!

With superhuman effort I bit my lip to hold in my hysterical chortles. As I bent to help him up, he sprang up red in the face. Ignoring my efforts to brush the mud and leaves from his trousers, he frantically looked around, "Where the devil is my briefcase?" We looked, mystified, in vain. Then I happened to look upwards. Not trusting myself to speak for the laughter welling up inside me I pointed with a shaky finger. Lodged in the branches of the Luxton's beech tree was Dr Britons briefcase!

There then followed an hilarious ten minutes of me finding a nearby gardener, who not only brought a ladder but, kindly, retrieved the briefcase. I'm sure the Doctor knew I was about to burst into hysterical laughter but he just curtly nodded towards me. "Sister." He said, then got into his car and drove away. I sat in mine and shook with pent up mirth. I must have laughed for several minutes as I had to wipe the tears from my eyes before I could drive on and finish my morning. What had amused me the most was Dr Britons reaction when his briefcase was retrieved. Ignoring his own bruises and damp trousers, he muttered: "Thank goodness! It could have been broken!" when the kindly gardener handed him his rescued briefcase.

A lot of the time I mourn the old days. With hindsight the standard of care seemed higher, people had more time; but some things weren't so good as today.

I used to visit a frail old couple in their eighties on a regular basis. Kitty was a small bird like creature needing regular iron injections for her pernicious anaemia. Alex was more robust but, as they were both elderly, we used to keep an eye on him too. He had a wonderful shock of iron grey hair and was commonly sat at the kitchen table when I arrived, wearing vest and braces. He would vainly try shaving a feeble downy growth on his face with a hand mirror held in a shaky hand. They lived in the bottom half of a large Victorian town house on the edge of the market town. The house had been converted to three flats and the old couple had lived there for over fifty years. They seemed devoted in every way and always seemed cheerful despite their obvious frailty.

One day Kitty was in bed when I arrived and was very poorly. Alex explained in his high pitched cracked voice how he found it difficult to wake her and she hadn't eaten since the previous breakfast time. The result was that we had to admit Kitty to the local cottage hospital where Alex would walk the mile up the hilly high street after lunch and sit by her bedside until 8pm, when he would walk back downhill home to their flat. Kitty had suffered a stroke and then she had a series of further strokes. Alex sat by her side all night on her last night as she slipped away peacefully.

About a month after her death I was passing the flat and had a few minutes to spare. There was a parking space right outside, so, on impulse, I pulled up and went in to see how Alex was coping.

He seemed delighted to see me and bade me sit as he reached for another coffee cup. While we drank he reminisced about his life with Kitty. Watching him closely, it came as no surprise when he revealed that, in fact he was Alexandria. He and Kitty were bright young things in the twenties and had fallen deeply and madly in love. The problem was their love was forbidden then, as they were both of the same sex. They had been rejected by both their families who said that it was against nature, a sin; it was a fad that would pass, and much more of the same. The girls decided to forget their families and move down to Sussex where Alex would pass herself off as a man so that they could live as man and wife.

Alex cut her hair in a man's style and dressed in men's clothes. They had made such a good job of it that none of their neighbours suspected and I would never enlighten them as to the truth. I could then see the soft downy fluff on Alex's face that she attempted to shave every morning. That would also account for the high pitched voice. I felt tears well up in my eyes. Alex patted my hand: "Cheer up Sister, I miss her too but we had more than fifty glorious years together, more than some conventional couples."

But I wasn't crying for the loss of Kitty, I was crying for a world which drove these lovers to go underground, made them feel that they had to live a lie rather than be proud of their deep and lasting love.

As I drove onto my next patient, I reflected on the tough decision Kitty and Alex had been forced to make. To have to leave their families and live a lie for over fifty years, just because they fell in love with the wrong person in the eyes of what society thought was acceptable. Yes, say what you like about the good old days, a few things have improved for the better now.

Florrie North

I pulled my ancient Morris over to the side of the lane, wound down the window, and switched off the engine. The view from the lane, with the fields and sea shimmering in the distance, was spectacular. I was able to look across to a small village. There was a haze in the air caused both by the heat and the unshed tears that had sprung, unbidden, into my eyes. I had just spotted the 'For Sale' sign outside the little lodge house by the entrance to Thorney Farm whilst driving through the village.

This was the mid-1970s, and I had been fortunate enough to secure a position as a district nurse in a particularly beautiful part of the country. I was serving a small market town, and all of its surrounding villages, at a time when the old country dialect was still being spoken by some of the older locals. I was especially pleased, as I had not been at all happy with the hustle and bustle of London nursing, where I had trained and spent several years. We (my husband, and I) had found a quiet, pretty, rural cottage in which to bring up our baby daughter. District nursing hours fitted very well around her nursery school.

One of the older locals, with an old fashioned country twang, was dear little Mrs North, latterly of Thorney Lodge, and the cause of the current lump in my throat. I knew that the 'For Sale' sign indicated that she had gone into residential care - something she had dreaded for some time - since being forced to leave her home of sixty eight years would undoubtedly signal the end for her. Sadly, this, ultimately, proved to be the case.

Stepping out of the car, I inhaled a huge fresh lungful of country spring air, poured a coffee from my flask, and leant back on the bonnet of the car to reflect, and admire the view.

Florence Funnel was born around 1888, the daughter of the head gardener on the, then, huge Thorney estate. She had one brother, Frank, best friends with a young man who worked on the farm. Henry North was some two years her senior and had begun working on the farm at the tender age of twelve. Their relationship progressed from mere friendship, pigtail pulling and apple scrumping to stepping out together, engagement and finally marriage when Florrie was twenty-two. By then the farm manager had purchased the larger part of the farm – the estate had been sold off in lots following the death of the squire. The twenty-four year old Henry was a good conscientious worker. 'Farmer' (as she always referred to him) promoted him to leading stocksman and allocated them the tiny lodge house on the edge of the estate.

I always loved the little lodge; it was tiny, but welcoming. I visited Florrie twice a week to dress a stubborn leg ulcer. On each visit she insisted on making coffee, which I accepted readily since she was fascinating company, and, I believed, I was one of the few people she saw with any regularity. I knew she relished the company. Coffee was always served in her best two bone china cups and saucers on a small wooden tray which was always adorned with a beautiful, clean and snowy white linen tray cloth.

She lived alone in the remote lodge, with only a radio for company, as she had done for many years since the death of, first, her brother Frank, and then Henry some twenty five years previously. Although extremely elderly by the time I knew her, Florrie was a thorough old countrywoman who knew where to hear the nightingales or where to find the first cuckoo. She could pluck and prepare a pheasant ready for the oven, pick hops and turn them into pillows to aid sleep, turn a collar on a shirt or 'sides to middle' a worn bedsheet. It was Florrie who first showed me how to make delicious (and potent) cottage cider from our windfalls without the need for a cider press.

Originally the little lodge had consisted of just two rooms with an outside privy. In the 1920s 'farmer' had given Henry permission to build a small porch-cum-boot-room to link the toilet to the back kitchen scullery, thus making it an integral part of the cottage. The farm had been very large but, in future years further parts of the farm were sold off by 'farmer's' descendants.

I would drive in to the right of the lodge where I could park on a piece of scrubland. This was part of the plot. The rest of the outside had been turned over to vegetables in Henry's day, but she was now beyond caring for this. I entered the lodge straight into the little boot-room with the privy to my left and Florrie's kitchen scullery to my right. Under the kitchen window was a small butler's sink with sloping wooden drainer and an 'Ascot' gas water heater over it. This was the only running water, and personal toilet was accomplished here as well as laundry and preparation of food. A small enamel topped table, with just two wooden chairs sat between the main door and the sink. Directly ahead, to the left of this door, on small legs, sat an ancient cooker, proudly bearing the legend 'New World'. An old wooden dresser with glazed doors formed the only other furnishing in the room. This held Florrie's few meagre provisions and crockery. A small walk-in larder lay to the left of this.

Once in the cottage, it was timeless. A glorious peace emanated from the whole place and, whilst it fronted a busy road, no sounds of this could be heard from within. Walking through into the main room from the kitchen, immediately to the right was a partition wall of match-boarding running almost the whole length of the room. There were several pictures and photographs hanging on the partition. Behind this was the sleeping accommodation. I only saw this once. I believe it consisted of a double feather bed at the end with a wardrobe at the bottom of it and against the wall.

To the right lay the main part of the sitting room. This had originally been one room and the partition had been put in many moons ago to create a private sleeping area. In the right hand corner was the heavy wooden front door leading straight out onto the road. It had been bolted closed many years ago, and was never used. A heavy long black velvet curtain covered this, which helped to silence the potential noise of the road with a deal of success – the only noise I remember hearing was the soporific ticking of the ancient mantle clock. To the left of the room was a very high inglenook fireplace which always seemed to have a roaring blaze. This was the only heating she used. Two high back Queen Anne style armchairs flanked the fireplace. Behind the far one was the only window in this part (it had originally been double aspect until the partition was installed). Under this was a small card table with a lace cloth upon which sat Florrie's radio set. A few ornaments decorated the high mantle shelf, and Florrie always insisted that I sat by the fire to enjoy my coffee.

It was on just such a morning that I first took notice of the pictures and photographs hanging from the partition. One in particular caught my attention. It was of an angelic looking little boy of around six or seven years old dressed in a sailor suit and with a mop of blond curls. "What a dear little chap. Who is he?" I asked, as Florrie appeared from the kitchen bearing the tray with our coffees.

"Oh, that is my son, Francis." She replied. I was somewhat taken aback, since I had not been aware of any surviving relatives.

"I didn't realise you had a son."

"Oh, my dear, why should you. He died from appendicitis when he was seven."

I must have appeared shocked – "I'm so sorry, Florrie. You didn't have any more children then?"

"Oh well, sister, how could we here? 'Tis far too small. 'Taint built for little ones. Farmer was good enough to let us stay on when Francis was born; though, by rights, he could have thrown us out."

She must have seen the pity in my face, for she said. "Ah, well, sister, these thing 'appen." Just like that! Calm acceptance of her lot. Knowing her place in society and not seeking to change it.

Young Henry North and Florrie had been married in 1910 and quickly settled into the lodge. They didn't think about a family

"In those days you considered yourself lucky if the farmer allowed married folk!" She told me.

Within four years Britain had declared war on Germany; Henry marched off to join his Regiment and to fight in Flanders. The night before he left, Florrie shed many tears. Despite Henry's optimistic opinion that the war would be all over by Christmas, she was well aware that there was a possibility that he might never come home. They clung together, they were very much in love and as she saw him off on the train the next day, Francis had already been conceived. By some miracle Henry survived the trenches and mustard gas. He knew from Florrie's letters that Francis had been born, he also knew that, had it not been for the war creating a great shortage of able bodied men, 'farmer' might have asked them to leave. They adapted the lodge with the partition, thanked 'farmer', and determined that Francis would be their only child. He grew into a sweet but weakly child. His days were spent either helping Florrie with the hop picking and baking, or helping his father with the calves. One fateful day in 1920 he awoke with a red face and high temperature. He had been complaining of tummy ache the night before, but, as he had eaten a surfeit of apples while helping to brew the cottage cider, she put the pain down to that. By lunchtime he was much worse. Florrie had tried all the remedies she knew and kept him in bed with a hot water bottle. By the time Henry got back to the lodge in the evening, poor little Francis was delirious! Henry sent for 'Farmer's' wife, who insisted that they must get the doctor.

"We will sort out his fee." She assured them. Dr Baker duly arrived; an ambulance was called and Francis was transported to the infirmary in the town. Florrie went with him. By the following morning the little lad had expired from a ruptured appendix.

"He lies in All Saints churchyard with his father. We bought a triple plot, see, Sister - we knew we would have no more."

Florrie and Henry settled down to the routine of life once more but kept him in their hearts and were thankful for his memory.

Now Florrie was to leave the little home she had sacrificed everything to stay in. I thought of the dissatisfaction in the world today, with everyone wanting to outdo their neighbours with bigger and better gadgets, houses and cars. Poor little Florrie North had been grateful for a roof and enough food to keep her and her beloved husband alive. Countless others of that generation had sacrificed much for king and country, yet asked, and got, little in return.

I knew it would not be long before she was reunited with Henry and her darling Francis, and, sadly, I was to be proved right. She died on Christmas Eve that year and now lies with her family in the little plot in All Saints - together again at last.

Some weeks after she left, Thorney Lodge was sold to a property developer. It is now a huge four bedroomed executive house with a manicured garden.

A Family Thing

My nursing rounds today, took me to a village on the beautiful forest. Jane had been a local child-minder, much loved she was known by all the local families. At the early age of sixty three she had lost her beloved husband of some forty five years. A year later she developed early onset Alzheimer's. Her eldest daughter Heather and her husband moved in with Jane to care for her at home for as long as possible. I called in from time to time to check that they were managing and to keep an eye on the progression of Jane's disease. Today, I sat and had a coffee with Heather, while she told me the following story.

The previous week, Heather had looked up and out of the attic window. Down below in the garden she saw her mum Jane sitting in the lounger, feet thrust out before her. Her newspaper flopped over her chest where she had dropped it as sleep overcame her.

Heather was still reeling. Her brain was trying to assimilate what she had just learned. Seeing Jane in the garden caused a succession of conflicting emotions to run through her. They ranged from disbelief to hatred and betrayal, then back to love and a fear of the future. Jane was newly diagnosed with

Alzheimer's and Heather was determined to keep her at home for as long as possible.

Jane and her husband Neil married when she was just eighteen and he a mere twenty. They moved in with Jane's mother and stepfather; Jane's natural father had died when she was ten years old. Her mother had remarried three years later and her younger sister followed within the year, then another sister and, finally, her baby brother. Jane and Neil's first child, Stephen, arrived within the first year of their marriage. When Stephen was six months old Jane's parents were killed in a car crash. It had happened one rainy night as they were on their way home from her stepfather's company dinner.

Jane's sisters and her brother had all been under five years old when her parents were killed. As Jane and Neil were living in the house with their own child, they became guardians of her younger siblings. They brought them up as their own and, when Stephen was three years old, Jane gave birth to Nancy.

The three siblings, being so young, always called Jane and Neil 'mummy and daddy' and treated Stephen and Nancy as their brother and sister.

Thus it happened that, at the tender ages of twenty one and twenty three respectively, Jane and Neil found themselves with five children to care for ranging from birth to eight years.

Life was a real struggle for the young couple. Jane's parents had owned the house and it had been covered by mortgage insurance, so the roof over their head was secure. There had been precious little insurance cover other than that. Any small monies left over covered the funerals of her mother and stepfather, but precious little else.

Neil was a newly qualified mechanic, so his wages were not high. To make ends meet Jane went early morning office cleaning, then took a college course in childcare in the evenings. Once she had passed her exams she became a childminder, so the small house was always bursting with noise, toys and children's tears and laughter. Jane, had never found the right moment to tell Heather and her other siblings the truth about her relationship to them. She dreaded causing them greater grief and was afraid of their reaction. So the years ran on.

As each of her siblings grew and moved out, Jane and Neil gave them a lump sum of cash to get them started in life. They had managed this by mortgaging the house, thereby giving each of them their rightful share. That meant that they still owed monies on the property in old age.

The years passed, the children grew and Neil and Jane retired. Heather and her husband moved in with them, to help out as they grew older and became frailer with the passage of time. Neil had finally died the previous year and now Heather had learnt that Jane would not get any better as her Alzheimer's took hold of her mind.

That morning, having settled Jane in the sunshine outside with her coffee and a newspaper, Heather went up into the attic room; the room that used to be Stephen, and her brother John's, bedroom. Nowadays it was a storeroom for cases of documents, photo albums and the Christmas decorations. Heather wanted to get Jane's affairs in order for her, while she still had some moments of lucidity. She wanted to find out her wishes for her funeral and she fancied that there may still be some financial loose ends to tie up. Jane had been very worried about her finances following Neil's death.

It was whilst she was sorting through the documents that she found it - the photo album with the pictures of Jane's parents in it. The documents included with it showed they were her parents also; hers and her brother and sister's parents!

Heather had a vague memory of them, but the way Jane spoke of them she had always assumed they were her grandparents. Now the truth was there, plain to see! How dare her mother - sister - whatever she was – Jane - keep this from them? She felt angry, betrayed, duped and wronged. Through blurry tears she looked out of the dormer window down upon the sleeping Jane. Then it all melted away; to be replaced by a feeling of utter love and gratitude. No wonder Jane was still struggling financially. She and Neil had given their lives to ensure that Heather and her siblings had enjoyed a happy and comfortable childhood. They had never wanted for anything; money was tight, but they were always well fed, clean and had decent clothes and shoes to wear. Their childhood had always been full of fun and laughter and her school friends had envied her for her young parents and houseful of other children to play with.

It was then that Heather realised the sacrifices Neil and Jane had made in order for them to have lived the life they had. They themselves had given up going out, as other young couples had. They had worked all hours and gone without themselves so that Heather and her siblings would never suffer due to the death of their parents. Neil and Jane <u>were</u> parents to them, in all but biological birth. She made up her mind that she would hide the documents away. She would not tell her siblings, her newly discovered niece and nephew or Jane, that she knew the truth. She also determined that she and her husband would pay off the outstanding mortgage on the house.

Seized with sudden love for her big sister – mother - Heather rushed downstairs and into the garden, just as Jane awoke from her nap. "Oh I must have dozed off!" Jane exclaimed, bleary eyed and dopey. Heather threw her arms around her and planted a big kiss on her papery cheek "Don't worry! I'll get you some fresh coffee. I love you Mum!" and she smiled at Jane as she picked up the cold coffee.

I drove away to my next patient, mulling over this new intelligence. On reflection it was clear that it really didn't matter who gave birth to you. It was who was there for you; who raised you and taught you how to be a caring human. That was all that mattered. That person could truly be called 'Mother'.

Sister at the Sharp End

I noticed early on in my career, that I functioned better as a nurse when things grew sticky; in other words in emergency situations. I had an ability to think on my feet, and stayed calm (at least outwardly).

I had really enjoyed my time as an anaesthetic nurse in theatre and was eventually to become a Resuscitation Officer, leading cardiac arrest teams and teaching staff on their annual life support training. But, before then, I had a brief spell working in an Urgent Treatment Centre, which was nurse led and G.P. run.

We had some odd encounters. One which springs readily to mind was the evening that a gentleman walked in clutching his face in both his hands and groaning loudly. I asked him, "What seems to be the trouble, sir?"

It was apparent that he had very little English, but he rolled his head from side to side still clutching his cheeks and groaning even more. "Is it a toothache?" I asked, coaxingly, trying to be helpful. There was more groaning from him. "Sadly we don't have a dental department here, but I can refer you straight away to the Emergency Dental Service up at the County?" At this he just groaned even more and stamped his foot impatiently.

"Can I call a taxi for you? I can ring ahead. They may see you straight away? " He rolled his eyes at me and at that point the desk clerk poked me in the side and handed me a piece of paper upon which he had written – 'penis stuck in trouser zipper!'

After my blushing apologies, there then followed an agonising (for the patient) fifteen minutes spent with the duty G.P. and myself plus a large pot of Vaseline until the doctor finally managed to free the zipper. No wonder our forebears preferred button flies! I have dressed wounds in easier places I must confess, but eventually our gentleman went off home a little more comfortable than when he had arrived. It is little wonder after my experiences with live patients that I preferred to pursue a career where I was dealing with the clinically dead in the form of those requiring resuscitation!

I recall the case of our postman, Kevin B. We had, in our village, two postmen. They worked opposite shifts to each other. As both were called Kevin and to distinguish one from the other we referred to them by the initials of their respective surnames – Kevin B and Kevin M.

One day I was working in the Urgent Treatment Centre when Kevin B brought his wife in. She was nursing a huge bump on her forehead, a suspected broken wrist and concussion. Since the wrist required an X-ray, and this was a Saturday, we needed to send her up to the County Hospital, but I was somewhat intrigued to notice her skin was shiny and sticky and her t-shirt seemed wet and clung to her in a rather odd fashion. Kevin claimed that she had fallen out of bed and banged her head on the bedside cabinet. I was reluctant to believe him.

Having sent her off, we were busy with other patients and I thought no more about it until I had to take in a parcel from Kevin M on the following Monday. Indeed my suspicions were right about Mrs B. She had sustained a colles fracture of her left wrist, had been concussed, bruised and generally banged up! Kevin M. couldn't wait to tell me the real reason for her condition.

It seemed that he and Kevin B had been talking about the model girls in Playboy magazine and saying how they always looked shiny and wet, as though they had just been swimming - the beads of moisture slowly running down their bronzed skin. Kevin M told Kevin B that they had been liberally smothered in Vaseline for the photo shoot, to create this illusion. Kevin B found that this drove him into some sort of sexual frenzy so, purchasing a huge pot of Vaseline, he encouraged his missus to smother herself in the stuff and get into bed with him on Saturday morning whilst the children were at their football club. Jumping onto the bed together he shouted: "Geronimo!" and grabbed at her in a sudden burst of passion. Unfortunately she slipped right out of his grasp and onto the floor thus colliding painfully with the bedside cabinet on the way! Bundling her up in her dazed state, he helped her to dress. He then encouraged her into the car and brought her up to the local hospital! Ever after this incident, which Kevin M couldn't wait to spread to all and sundry around the area, Kevin B was referred to as 'Vaseline' and Kevin M as just 'Kevin'. Poor Mrs B!

Another embarrassing incident involving a broken wrist came from our respectable local insurance man, Mr Glasscock. Mr and Mrs Glasscock lived in a bungalow on the outskirts of the small country town which housed our cottage hospital. There had been a spate of shed burglaries in the locality. When Mr Glasscock came into the Urgent Treatment Centre with his broken arm, he explained that he had fallen out of their bedroom window whilst trying to see if they were being burgled as Mrs Glasscock had heard a noise late the previous night.

As I was going off duty that evening I met Phil, our porter, in the hospital car park. "I see Brittledick has busted his arm then, Sister!" he confided, with some degree of satisfaction. "You know I can't discuss individual patients with you, Phil." I replied (somewhat tartly) "Well here's how it really happened, Sister!"

He ignored my remark and proceeded to tell me the following tale (related to him by Mrs Glasscock). It seemed that they slept at the front of their bungalow and they had a side gate leading to the back garden and shed. Both the Glasscocks slept au naturel (i.e. naked). Now Mrs Glasscock had been rattled by the recent theft of her neighbour's bicycle from his garden shed during one of the nights.

Hearing a rattling on the dustbins outside, she nagged Mr Glasscock so much that he threw open the window and leant out to see what the cause was. It appeared it was only next door's cat jumping up onto their garden wall, but as he leaned across Mrs Glasscock to peer out of the window, she was filled with devilment. Seeing his naked behind, she couldn't resist tickling it and exclaiming "wheeoo!" as she did so! This caused him to jump so much that he shot out of the window onto the front shingle of the drive and straight onto his arm. He had also sustained a left colles fracture!

I am not sure how I kept a straight face at the time, but I said: "Phil! Don't you ever let me hear that you have spread rumours about Mr Brittle – I, I mean Mr Glasscock - and his injury. Remember patient confidentiality!" Then mustering some fake dignity I got into my car and started it up; but driving home was difficult as I was crying with laughter!

I later heard that Phil, ever the soul of indiscretion, had told me the true tale of the Glasscocks as related at the WI by Mrs Glasscock herself! No wonder I eventually went into clinical teaching.

Sister in Transition

The old cottage hospital had served the little market town for almost a century. It had been a reassuring bastion of hope and care for the residents of the town, bringing comfort and healing to the sick. Now the town had outgrown it.

The town had been earmarked for redevelopment in the late 1970's. Two new housing estates had been built between 1974 and 1982. The little hospital was no longer able to cope with the numbers. It had a small minor injury department, eleven medical beds and six surgical beds. The theatre opened for day cases just four mornings a week. It had suffered the cloud of closure hanging over its head for a few years, not helped by the brand new district general hospital which had opened in the big seaside town sixteen miles to the south.

Not that the populace wanted to lose it. Many a petition was signed in support of it staying. Staff and patients alike raised money and lobbied the local MP. The problem was, the site it was on was too small to expand and land prices had rocketed since the building regime in the town.

At that time I worked part time on the community as a district nurse. One of my patients was little Mrs Simkin. She lived with her daughter and son in law, Mr and Mrs Brace, on a beautiful farm on the southern outskirts of the town. Mr Brace was one of the largest arable farmers in the county and one of the most "hands on" that I ever knew. Every time I visited his mother in law he would be harrowing or dumping slurry in the pit. Sometimes I would see him in the distance in the middle of a field in his tractor. Not that he didn't have plenty of help. He was one of the biggest local employers.

Mrs Brace always made me coffee after I had tended to her mother, we would have a pleasant chat for a few minutes before I set off on my rounds. One morning she dropped into the conversation her concerns for Alan, Mr Brace. "He keeps getting a dull ache in his right side Sister. Just below the ribs I asked him to let you examine him but he wouldn't stay, just told me not to fuss"

I advised her to get him checked out at the surgery, but we both knew he would be too stubborn for that. The time came within a few months that Mrs Simkin succumbed to the cancer that consumed her frail ageing body and passed away. The morning she died Mr Brace was in the kitchen supporting his grieving wife. I was shocked when I saw him. His face was yellow and he had lost several stone in weight since I saw him last. I finally persuaded him to seek help, but his pancreatic cancer was too advanced; It had spread to his liver. He lived for only ten months after the death of his mother in law.

Mrs Brace carried out the wishes of her husband. The farm was divided into three. One third was sold to a large building company and a third large housing estate sprawled across the beautiful fields that once spouted crops. I always felt a tug at the heartstrings whenever I drove past the houses spoiling my view of undulating fields that had once been there.

The middle portion was sold as a smallholding, boasting a farm shop, butchers and a small equestrian centre. Mrs Brace had been well provided for. She moved away to live near her sister in Gloucestershire, but not before she had carried out the last of her husband's wishes and handed the last third of the farm to the people of the town as the site for their brand new state of the art community hospital!

This generous act ensured the security of the town's hospital and also brought all the services under one roof. The new hospital had its own theatre, operating five days a week on day-case surgery. It had a huge minor injury unit, its own radiography department, physio and dental departments. Mother and baby clinics could be held in the big clinical education room and it had a huge outpatient section too.

The little cottage hospital at the north end of the High Street was turned into warden assisted flats for the elderly. It always brought a lump to my throat whenever I went into the main entrance as on the wall was a large plaque stating that the hospital was made possible by the kind generosity of Mr and Mrs Alan Brace. He would have hated the publicity!

Another example of change was the smallholding that Jesse ran with her ageing mother. Jesse and her mum, Mrs Kenton, had about four acres in a village just outside the town. Jesse kept her two elderly horses there but mostly they grew vegetables and flowers which they sold on site. Their bungalow was small but spotless and as Mrs Kenton became more frail and ill, I would spend time after my ministrations chatting to Jesse and having coffee.

We would mainly enjoy horsey talk as Jesse knew I had a big warmblood mare. Often I would bring carrots and fuss her horses, and she always enjoyed the chats over coffee. I think I was one of the few people she had time to chat with.

Inevitably her mother died and Jesse carried on with the business. She implored me to still stop by and have coffee with her but time runs on when there are patients to see. I did stop a couple of times and had a cosy coffee and chat but my visits became less frequent I am sorry to say.

One time I was passing and could only see one horse in the field. On impulse I swung into the drive. Jesse was bent over watering some plants. She straightened up and smiled when she saw me. I followed her into the bungalow. While waiting for the kettle she told me how she had lost 'Prince' to a bad case of colic the previous month. "Gut twisted you see, sister. Nothing they could do, he was twenty-five years old anyway." But I could see the sorrow in her eyes.

'Blue', her other horse was nearly thirty. I wondered how she would take the loss of her horsey companion.

A few weeks later I was passing by and noticed a 'For Sale' sign outside the gate. I pulled the wheel of my ancient Morris around and drove up the drive.

Jesse was delighted to see me. Over coffee she explained how she had gone out one morning to feed Blue and found her looking peaceful, but stone dead, in her field. "She just looked asleep, sister." She said "Must have been her heart, so sudden I'm sure."

She told me that she had found the business too much for her. She had only kept it on so as to provide a home for the horses. She was moving into one of the small flats in the market town. "Cheaper to run and handy for the shops and things." She explained with a smile. I wasn't convinced it was what she really wanted but I think financially it was her only option.

I never saw her again. The little family business became a small light industrial unit housing a tyre depot and a picture-framers. I could never drive past it without a pang of sorrow thinking about Jesse, Prince and Blue. Sometimes change is not always for the best.

Nurse on the District

"Three weeks? Just to get someone to shop for her twice a week?" I stared at my colleague in disbelief. We were discussing a patient who was admitted to the local community hospital following a fall. Florence had not been injured other than a bit of minor bruising, but the time had come to adapt her cottage, and get her some help if she were to retain her independence.

Florence was eighty-nine years old and lived in a small two up two down cottage with no proper heating and lethal cottage stairs. Her stay in hospital need only have been a few days, but we could not let her go home until social services had moved her bed downstairs into one of the two rooms and sorted out someone to clean and shop for her once a week. Fortunately, she had a downstairs toilet and shower room and used her walking frame to get around. That, with meals on wheels delivered daily would keep her going in her own home a little longer.

The problem was, that social services needed so many forms filled out in order to approve the help Florence needed that it meant her having an unnecessary stay of nearly a month in hospital until she could go home with the correct support in place. This would take about three weeks to organise!

As I drove to my next patient, my mind went back to my days as a trainee District nurse in the mid- seventies in the East End of London. We organised most things ourselves then, with no form filling and precious little trouble. I reminisced about some of the cockney characters I had the pleasure to care for in those far off happy days.

*****

"You 'ave a nice hot drink while this cold weather is on, nurse, dear!" said Mrs Copthorne as she shuffled in from the kitchen to her scullery with a tray. Mrs Copthorne lived in an old Victorian terrace house on a street in Hackney, the East end of London, which was destined for demolition.

This street had been badly damaged in the blitz during the war. The houses still standing all had a demolition order on them and most were now empty. Mrs Copthorne's house was split into two dwellings. The upstairs flat was now vacant. Mrs Copthorne had the downstairs, which consisted of a big front room used as her bedroom, the original breakfast room was now her sitting room, mostly unused with her best china knick knacks and treasured photos in. The back room was the kitchen scullery which she mostly lived in. Off of this were the steps to the cellar

74

which housed her only running water, an ancient brass cold tap. At the back of the kitchen was a door leading to the courtyard and the only toilet for the house - an outdoor shack with an old wooden bench lavatory with a pull chain. All her ablutions were done at the kitchen sink.

I felt bad her making me coffee as I knew she had to go up and down the steep cellar stairs to fill the kettle, but she always insisted. I think she valued the company as she always made it an occasion. The tray would be lined with a snowy linen cloth, she used her finest bone china cups and saucers and there were always rich tea biscuits on a bone china plate. It made the hot instant coffee taste much better than usual. I liked Mrs Copthorne, widowed during the first war, she had lived in this road ever since and knew everybody there. She refused to even consider the modern alternative accommodation she was offered.

We worried about her, she had to move, but when and where was as yet, undecided. I was training as a District nurse and went into Mrs Copthorne three times a week to dress her ulcerated leg. She had very little, just her widow's pension as far as I knew, yet was always insistent that I had coffee and biscuits with her. Since retiring from the local factory, where she cleaned, she would walk daily to the local church hall for her pensioner's lunch and a social chat with old friends and neighbours. It was called "Gospel Hall" but this was beyond the capability of her tongue as she always called it 'Gopsel 'all' much to my amusement.

I enjoyed talking with these elderly characters. They were walking history books. I learnt much of what life had been like in the Edwardian days of their childhoods. I discovered how hard it had been during the blitz, the bombing raids that had claimed the lives of their friends and neighbours during the second war.

It was Mrs Copthorne herself who told me of the local Doctor, who rushing to help when the local cinema had taken a direct hit one Saturday morning and dug out the bodies of his own two children from the rubble. These lovely old folk had lived through much sorrow, fear and hardship. They had very little but were always cheerful and chipper and ready to share whatever they had with anyone who came into their homes.

Today as we sipped our coffee I asked her if she had been offered anywhere to live that took her fancy? "No, nurse." She said gloomily, "They are all up in the sky. Why would I want to live up on the tenth floor, having to get into one of those metal lift contraptions, just to get to me front door, and I couldn't get to Gopsel 'all from any of them; not that I can go today!" "Why-ever not?" I asked with surprise, for Mrs Copthorne never missed the lunches. It appeared that her only pair of shoes had a hole in the sole and she would not lower her standards and go in her slippers. "I shall have to wait for my nephew to pick me up on his monthly visit and take me to the cobblers to get them repaired" she said. I finished my coffee "For goodness sake give them to me" I insisted, I can get them back for you before midday today"

Mrs Copthorne looked ready to cry. "Oh! Nurse would you? I should be so grateful." And she fumbled in the drawer for her purse. I waved it aside, "Sort it when I get back with them." I replied, then, grabbing the brown paper bundle containing the shoes, I left to continue my round.

It was a small matter to drop them at the local cobblers shop and explain that I wanted express service. I went on to my next patient - I should explain that we student district nurses walked everywhere in London in those days. I would pick them up later that morning.

I dropped them back to a grateful Mrs Copthorne in plenty of time for her to walk to her beloved Gopsel 'all for her lunch. It was hardly out of my way, took no more than a few extra minutes and was the easiest solution. No nonsense and all sorted speedily in a sensible manner. These days the nursing staff would not be allowed to do this. Instead social services would have to arrange a weekly shopper to take them and that would involve endless form filling and assessments. Progress doesn't always mean a more efficient system.

Mrs Copthorne eventually had to leave her beloved home and friends. They put her into a fifth floor flat. It was centrally heated and had running hot and cold water, but Mrs Copthorne hated it. Volunteers collected her once a week to take her to Gopsel 'all, but it was never the same for her; she no longer knew the area that had been her home for over fifty years. She died within six months of moving.

In those days I had a patient living on the tenth floor of one of these modern blocks of flats. Mrs Edwards had also been forced to move when her street was demolished. She now lived in "Harper House" and tried very hard to make the best of it. At 85 she had been forced to make big adjustments to live in a high rise building including overcoming her fear of lifts. She had done very well, but didn't go out very much because of it.

This particular day, I arrived to do her dressings. I headed to her bathroom to wash my hands as always when Mrs Edwards became concerned. "Oh! Nurse, would you use the kitchen sink please, it's not nice in the bathroom today." I immediately sensed something wrong. On questioning her it appeared that her toilet had not been able to flush for several days. She had made the considerable effort to go down in the lift and walk to the telephone box on the corner to report it to the local council but nothing had yet been done. This necessitated her carrying in buckets of water from the bigger kitchen sink, to tip down the toilet herself to clear it. This she was doing three times a day. It was too much for her at her advanced age. I took the number and promised to chase it up and report it myself, which I duly did as soon as I got back to our office.

Imagine my anger then, when on visiting the following week I caught her in the act of struggling along her hallway with a bucket from the kitchen. "Still no joy?" I asked, "No, nurse, no one's been near to fix it, and I am up to date with my rent." She looked pale, tired and worried. "Right!" I said. "Leave it to me!" I was furious. I finished my morning round and walked out of my way to the local council offices. Demanding to see someone in a position of authority I drew myself up to my full five feet four inches and sticking out my twenty-two year old chin I read them the riot act finishing with threats to report them to the public health authority (although I had no idea how to do that or who to report to).

The poor clerk receiving this tirade was so apologetic he almost wrung his hands, then I strode out with my most efficient nurses walk!

The following week I visited Mrs Edwards, she beamed when she saw me "Oh nurse, I don't know how you did it but they came and fixed the flush the very next day."

I smiled, "We are not without some influence you know!" I told her, smiling smugly.

There were some funny moments during those few months of training. I had already qualified as a nurse when a friend, a fellow freshly fledged nurse, and I were offered the chance to do the district nurse training. Some of it was spent in the classroom where our lovely tutor did her best to make us feel easy with the study. When not in class we would be out on the rounds visiting patients, but we usually had an hour or more in the middle of the day when we could meet for lunch.

Our training hospital, from which we had just qualified, had arranged for us to have our meals at the local hospital, St Leo's, in Hackney. The canteen there was spacious and there was always plenty of choice of hot or cold meals. In those days, money was scarce for a very junior nurse and we always seemed to be hungry.

One Sunday we found ourselves free to meet up for lunch. The menu was roast chicken with roast potatoes, vegetables and bread sauce, followed by semolina and strawberry jam! Fortunately I have always disliked semolina!

The food smelt wonderful as we walked into the canteen. It was cold outside. We had been on our feet all morning and were starving. The kitchen staff at St Leo's were mainly from overseas. The staff serving often had very little English (if any) and that proved to be the case today.

Fran and I got our chicken and sat at the table with a couple of the girls we recognised from the year above us at St Cuthbert's. I could never abide bread sauce, so I tucked into the delicious meal with relish, but two mouthfuls into her meal, Fran pulled a face: "Yeuk!" she pronounced, "They have put semolina on my chicken!" By now the others had discovered that also. One of them, who had chosen salad, was already onto her pudding course. She jumped up, crossly. "Yes!" She retorted. "And bread sauce with strawberry jam to follow!"

I laughed really hard as Fran and the others got up to complain. "On your way back with your salad, Fran, could you please bring me a yoghurt for pudding?" It caused much merriment once their appetites had been slated, but it made us more cautious the next time we ate there.

The East End has changed beyond recognition nowadays. Hackney has been gentrified and very few of the old cockney folk remain. The shops are so cosmopolitan that you could be in any country in any part of the world. It is true to say that there are no longer the appalling living conditions and social deprivation that once existed, but, Oh! How I miss the Mrs Copthornes and the Mrs Edwards of my early nursing days!

Sister above stairs

The big house looked intimidating. A huge Georgian mansion set in several acres of park land up a long drive. The first time I came here to visit Mr Tate I had instinctively gone round to the back door. I assumed it was a tradesman's entrance, but Mr Tate wouldn't hear of it.

"No, Sister," he said "we are honoured to have your services and very lucky indeed to have our fine NHS. You use the front door in future and make sure the staff look after you"

Mr Tate was a gruff Lancastrian, who had inherited the family's vast cotton empire. Now semi-retired, he still sat on the board but had moved to the milder climes of Sussex some years previously, leaving the running of the company to his only son Julian. The beautiful estate that they had bought doubled as a company office and he had staff, both domestic and company, working there.

I was visiting three times a week to dress his ulcerated legs. He never allowed me to leave without going into the snug next to the main hall where his secretary would join me for coffee. Really nice freshly brewed coffee, laid out on a silver tray with bone china cups and homemade biscuits. This morning Julian was home and he joined us (much to my concern).

I liked Julian and he liked me, but that was the problem. He liked me a bit too much and was always trying to get me to go out with him, even though he knew I was happily married. The other problem was that he had a speech impediment and spoke with such a mouthful of plums as to render his banter virtually unintelligible!

This morning he mumbled something incomprehensible finishing with a gruff "Wot wot?" and chuckling while slapping me on the knee and squeezing it, winking at me the while.

I felt myself reddening and muttered a polite "yes" smiling politely, at this he roared with laughter while Joan, Mr Tate's secretary rolled her eyes at me and we sipped our coffee in uncomfortable silence - me, wondering exactly what I had agreed to! That day I got out of there as soon as I could, dodging Julian's hand as he attempted to slap my bottom laughing and muttering words I could only guess at. I jumped into my car and sped away quickly, my tongue burning from rushing the scalding hot coffee in an attempt to escape.

My next call was very different. It was to Bella O'Brien a traveller lady who lived in an old Gypsy caravan in the grounds of the Fairchild's house. Mr Fairchild was a futures broker, a man of wealth and the owner of a large executive detached house on the prestigious gated Bitterne estate. His house stood in almost an acre. Why Mrs O'Brien was there at all was a mystery, but rumour had it that the Fairchild's had taken pity on her homeless plight and allowed her to pitch her old wooden caravan in the grounds of their home.

I was fond of Bella and her little home. It was tiny, but bright and clean. Her only heating was from the tiny coal stove which doubled as her cooking range. She had just the one chair and her bed, a small wooden bunk, was at the back of the unit. All around the walls hung brass spoons, horse brasses and ornaments of all descriptions. The tiny cabin was decorated with flowery wallpaper inside and beautiful painting outside. Her water came from a big jug and basin on her small bedside cupboard, heated in her kettle on the range. Phoebe Fairchild kindly allowed me to go into the main house to wash my hands at each visit.

I was told on my first visit to go round the back and through the back door which Phoebe called the tradesman's entrance. Phoebe always spoke with an affected accent, attempting to sound upper class but dropping her H's at times and mispronouncing certain words. Despite her kindness in letting the lady live in her garden, Phoebe spoke of Bella with some degree of shame, as though having her there was somehow degrading to their family.

That morning I was shocked at Bella's leg. It was so much worse - red and swollen. She looked flushed. I took her temperature. It was raised; clearly she had picked up an infection in her ulcer. Looking around the little cabin my heart fell. The entrance was just a thick canvas curtain with a velvet curtain hung on the inside. Keeping clean was a problem with no proper toilet facilities and no running water. There was the possibility that I could ask Phoebe if she would have her in the house, but I feared I would need to get Bella admitted to the local cottage hospital for a few days to clear this infection up.

I broached the subject with Bella. "I'm not going in there with them!" she said forcefully. "If I have to leave here for a while I might go into the hospital, Sister, but not the house!"

I popped in to Phoebe to ask to use the house phone. I appraised her of the situation and asked if she knew of any of Bella's relatives that might need to be informed. There were pictures of a toddler in silver frames in her cabin and I fancied that she had a daughter somewhere. "Don't worry about that, Sister." said Phoebe, "I'll sort all that out."

After a few calls to the Doctor and then the hospital matron, I booked the transport ambulance and went back to tell Bella of the arrangement.

Some days later I popped into the cottage hospital to collect more supplies for my rounds. I decided to pop into the ward to see Bella as I thought she might be lonely in there.

To my delight, I saw Phoebe Fairchild sitting by her bed chatting to her. Bella had flowers and grapes on her bedside locker. Not wishing to disturb them I crept out and almost collided with Sister Lorriner, the senior sister at the cottage. I told her how pleased I was that Mrs Fairchild was visiting Bella. "I am surprised she has bothered, I was always under the impression that she thought herself far too posh for the likes of poor Bella and only allowed her to stay out of a sense of Noblesse oblige." I said.

Irene Lorriner smiled wryly, she had lived in the town all her fifty two years and knew everyone and everything- she snorted "Huh!" she said. "It's the least she can do, to visit her poor old mother, after making her live in a caravan in the garden!" I was shocked. "You don't mean.." I began. "Yes!" Replied Irene, "Bella is Phoebe's mother, but she won't thank you for spreading that about, thinks she's too high and mighty for that. Bella won't go into sheltered accommodation and Phoebe won't have her in the house. Bella loves her little caravan, so they compromise."

I thought of the contrast as I walked back to my car. Mr Tate with his big house, fortune and down to earth approach to life and Phoebe, putting on her airs and graces, living a life totally different from the one she was born to - ashamed of her roots.

In the words of Mr Tate: "Nowt so strange as folk!" I thought to myself.

A Wonderful Husband

I drove through the big Iron gates onto Bitterne Park, the large gated estate known locally as Millionaires Row. Mr and Mrs Jones lived in a large, mock-Tudor house set in about an acre and a half of landscaped gardens.

Mr Jones was a retired bank manager and, sadly, had suffered a series of strokes over the previous five years, leaving him partially paralysed and bringing on early dementia. Mrs Jones was his main carer with help from us district nurses. Their only son had married then emigrated to South Africa, where he held a very lucrative position in a big international company. Sally, their elderly, scruffy but affectionate, mongrel dog was the only other occupant of the huge house.

Usually Mrs Jones left the front door unlocked for me and I would let myself in every morning for my daily visit to David, her husband. Sally would greet me, wagging her little tail furiously and bouncing around my ankles with joy. This morning it was quiet when I entered.

"Cooee!" I called. "Anyone home?" Mrs Jones came out of the front room looking downcast. Her eyes were red rimmed from crying, she was pale and had not yet put on her customary face powder and lipstick. "Oh, sister!" She quavered "I had to have the vet round this morning and he has had to put Sally to sleep." She broke down at that point and fell onto my shoulder, wracked with sobs. I put my arms around her, but being an incurable lover of all animals I'm afraid I sobbed with her.

After a few minutes she straightened up, wiping her eyes and we both blew our noses. "I'll put the coffee on." She said, bustling into the kitchen. I went through into the bedroom to begin my care of David.

Mrs Jones was a tall, slim, naturally elegant lady of around seventy years. Her beautiful coiffured white hair and blue eyes gave her a very striking appearance. She always kept herself, David, and the house in apple pie order. She was highly intelligent and played bridge with friends, but only if they came to her. She wouldn't leave David on his own. She popped out to the shops twice a week when her cleaning lady came to keep an eye on him. That was her only outing. Once a year she would allow us to put David into a care home for respite care whilst she visited Marcus, her son, and his family in South Africa. She was entitled to regular respite every six weeks but wouldn't hear of it.

We nurses went in daily to help Mrs Jones get David out of bed and to help her with his toilette. He said very little and often was unaware of what was going on around him. He had been known to lash out and become violent with Mrs Jones at times. Like most victims of severe stroke, he could get very frustrated. This morning he may have sensed that something was wrong as he was a bit more impatient than usual. We were helping him to dress and as we were putting on his shoes and socks he kicked out at Mrs Jones, nearly knocking her over as she knelt at his feet. Between us we got him from the bathroom into his wheelchair and took him into the lounge.

He had been a keen golfer, so whenever golf was on the television Mrs Jones would switch it on for him to watch. She did this on that particular morning then disappeared into the kitchen to fetch the tray of coffee for us. I listened to the golfing commentary then asked: "David, what's a birdie?" Straightway came the answer, clear as a bell: "One under par!" So he still had the odd moment of lucidity. Mrs Jones came back in with coffee. David's was in a feeding cup as he was unable to feed himself. We sat in companionable silence drinking our coffee for a while watching the golf. Mrs Jones was feeding David, suddenly he seized her wrist, pinching as hard as he could with his "good" hand, knocking the coffee from her grasp and making her squeal with pain! "No! There now David! No, you mustn't do that." I soothed, as Mrs Jones mopped up the coffee. Leaving David safely in his chair watching the golf, I followed her into the kitchen.

91

She stood at the sink holding her red wrist under cold running water. I put my arm around her shoulders. "You know we can find a permanent placement in a nice care home for David? You shouldn't have to put up with this." I told her.

She smiled at me. "Bless you, Sister!" she said. "I know you all care and we are both very grateful for the help, but I couldn't betray him like that. No, I vowed until death do us part and I mean to keep that vow. What you see now isn't my David. The man I married was a devoted brilliant father, a good provider and a wonderful husband. I do this for him, the David I love and married, Marc's father, not the wreck of humanity we see today."

I felt really moved by those words and I pondered on them as I drove on to my next visit. That was surely what true love was about. Not racing pulses and lustful desire, but a deep understanding and unconditional love and devotion.

Some months after this David suffered another big stroke and died. He was at home with Mrs Jones until the end.

A few weeks after his death I was coming out of the high street bank when I met Mrs Jones. She looked elegant as always but radiant and very happy. I asked after her. "I'm great, Sister!" She enthused. "Now I am free I have put the house on the market and Marc has invited me to live with them in South Africa. My solicitor is handling the sale of the house and effects. I am packed up to go, all my large bits and pieces are being shipped over. I fly out in two weeks. I'm so glad to have seen you to say a big thank you and my goodbyes."

This was the reason she had never replaced Sally, this is why she was so dutiful to David, she had done her grieving over the years following his strokes. His death had released them both. She wanted to do right by him until the end. She had achieved this very well, but now was <u>her</u> time, she could join her beloved son and grandchildren and have some life at last.

I hugged her and genuinely wished her well. I never saw her again, but I think of her often. I am sure she found happiness and appreciation at last.

Sister on the Spot

"Polly, wake up! It's the mad rapist!" I whispered into her left ear. Polly Pottinger opened one eye: "Oh good! Some excitement at last!" These were the sort of comments from my patients that I relished. It demonstrated the humour and spirit of the lovely people I was privileged to work with.

Polly was a charming lady of some seventy eight years and possessed of a dry sense of humour but in the later stages of multiple sclerosis. The disease had robbed her of the use of her legs leaving her confined to a wheelchair in the little bungalow she called home.

Her only companion was a large fractious ginger tomcat, Moses. Not that Polly was lonely; rumour had it that she had maintained a forty year love affair with her old boss, a local widower, who visited her every day and loved her deeply, yet she would never marry him. He had passed away some four years previously so now it was us district nurses who visited Polly twice daily to help her out of bed and then to help her back again in the evening. The home-help would come twice weekly and she had meals-on-wheels delivered every day.

It was a quiet, remote, place; just a short walk from the village. We begged her to have keys cut for us and to lock the doors, but she wouldn't hear of it. "No need, dear! The back door's never locked!" And with that we had to be content. This "back door job", as we nurses called it, was a common way for our patients to allow us access. Some would hang their front door keys on a long piece of string inside the front door to be pulled through the letterbox and used as needed. These practices worried me, I felt they were a huge security risk for some of the most vulnerable people, yet, remarkably, they all stayed safe. This was the 1970's, an era long before digital keypads and such modern gadgets.

In those days most semi-rural or rural areas still had a fairly low crime rate and neighbours still looked out for each other. While I helped Polly I made a huge fuss of Moses rubbing his ear. Today he was in an amiable mood and rolled onto his back purring. I quit while I was ahead! His favourite ploy was to lure the unsuspecting into giving him a tummy tickle, which then resulted in him suddenly curling around their hand and removing chunks of skin with his teeth and claws! "Sorry, old mate" I told him "I've fallen for that one before!" So my work continued.

It was a typical shift in my working week. I felt very lucky to be doing my work in such wonderful localities. Sussex was varied in landscape, but with pretty, peaceful villages, small country towns, plenty of sheep and wild birds plus hospitable, interesting people.

At that time the roads were quieter and the pace of life slower. I pulled over in one of my favourite spots for coffee. I got out of the car and perched on the edge of the bonnet. As I unscrewed the lid of my flask the inquisitive sheep came over to the edge of their field to see what goodies I might have. There were groups of lapwings browsing amongst them. I saw the blue sky with the upper tree branches looking black as they waved in the breeze. The coffee was good and hot, the only sound was of the gentle wind and the sheep. In the distance there was a little church spire peering above the hedgerow. I thought then that this could have been anywhere in England in any century. I felt wonderfully at peace and in love with the world.

Soon I was brought back to earth! I had arranged to meet the new GP, Dr Nye, at the beautiful house of Mrs Coates. She was the wealthy widow of a newspaper editor - a very autocratic lady, intelligent and with a very sharp wit. She had a stubborn chest infection which seemed impervious to the penicillin thrown at it. Dr Nye wanted to examine her for himself, as his predecessor had been treating her, unsuccessfully, until his retirement the previous week.

The investigation involved a rather intimate examination of her back and chest so a female professional chaperone would assist in maintaining her dignity; also Mrs Coates was now in her 80's and had a tendency to become confused at times. Her housekeeper let me in. "Ah! Good-day, Sister, How wonderful to see you." Mrs Coates smiled graciously at me, pointedly ignoring her housekeeper. One never knew whether she was being serious - her humour was very droll - or if she was cross or, perhaps, confused.

She had dug in her heels about going into hospital, so I was visiting her daily to check on her progress. I helped her into her best nightie and passed some eau-de-cologne spray to her - she always smelt pleasant and expensive. "I will not let myself go just because I am somewhat incapacitated!" She told me.

Dr Nye arrived and briefly introduced himself. He nodded to me, and I unbuttoned her nightie, He bared her chest and listened intently with his stethoscope, then he palpated her abdomen. We helped her to sit forward and he politely lifted her nightie up around her shoulders in order to apply the stethoscope again, which I noted, with approval, that he first warmed in the palm of his hands. Finally he felt her neck glands and placing a spatula on her tongue, he examined her throat. He scribbled a prescription for some different anti-biotics which he tore off with a flourish before handing it to me for collection later; then he wished her good-day and was gone. "Well, he seemed very nice." I remarked, as I helped her on with her slippers. "Who's that, dear?" replied Mrs Coates. "Dr Nye, your new GP." I told her. "Oh!" she said, looking puzzled: "Is that who it was? I thought the dear vicar was being a wee bit familiar!"

Old Friends

"Give my love to Miss Baines please, Sister."

Clara Craddock and Bessie Baines had been best friends since childhood. Whilst on first name terms with each other, they reverted to formal titles when talking to a third party. My travels as a District nurse in the 1970's around the Sussex Downs area brought me into contact with all kinds of people from all kinds of differing backgrounds. These two venerable old ladies were amongst my favourites. They had been born into wealthy middle class families and now both were well into their 80's. By design they lived next door to each other. They had spent their last few retirement years in one or the others' homes. They had always been close friends but, by the time I knew them, ill health and frailty meant that they were reduced to speaking to each other on the telephone or sending messages, both ways, through me on my visiting days.

Sometime previously I had remarked on an old photograph on Miss Craddock's sideboard. It showed a tennis party of young men and women circa 1912.

"Oh yes!" She said fondly, her eyes assuming a far-away look, "Those were the days." She sighed.

"We had such fun! "

When I pressed further she pointed out some of the young men.

"The three on the right are my brothers - only Arnold, the baby in the sailor suit, is still alive. Frederick we lost at Paschendale and Harry was killed at the Somme. The tall young man on the left was Arthur. Now, he was Miss Baines' fiancé! Next to him, on the left, that's his cousin Ernest. He was my fiancé. We lost them both at Ypres!"

She sighed and, smiling, added:

"They were such young rips! "

The sadness in their lives - and many more like theirs - lingered with me as I drove away from the two houses towards my next call.

Bessie Baines was the daughter of a local farmer of considerable acreage and means. She had become firm friends with Clara Craddock, the daughter of her father's solicitor. Their parents had pushed the girls together as suitable playmates from the ages of four or five, and they became inseparable friends. Bessie took on the role as farm secretary on the family farm as soon as she finished her education. Clara had proved to be a fine seamstress. She provided fine workmanship on the clothes of many of the local gentry. As the girls grew up they fell in with the sons and daughters of other middle class families in the area. They were seen at the local round of tennis parties, balls and tea dances. The Fanshawe Cousins, Arthur and Ernest, were both Lieutenants at the local school of musketry and they took an interest in the girls. Soon the couples were 'walking out' together. One day, in 1913, Bessie cycled the mile and a half to Clara's house. Her cheeks were bright red and her eyes were shining.

"Guess what, Clara?" She asked, but, without waiting for an answer, continued: "Arthur has asked me to marry him! We will marry next year!"

Clara hugged her. "How wonderful!"

The two girls spent a delicious hour discussing trousseaus, bridesmaids and honeymoons. The following Saturday, Clara met Ernest as usual. He seemed pre-occupied. They stopped by a bench in the park and Ernest turned to Clara —

"I don't know how to say this!" He muttered, looking embarrassed.

Clara's stomach knotted in apprehension. What would he say? Had he met someone else? Would he finish seeing her? He took her hand and knelt in front of her.

"Clara Craddock, will you do me the honour of becoming my wife – please? "

She felt some amusement, but didn't need to think about her answer. When next she met Bessie, their sole topic of conversation was their respective weddings the following year.

Clara had a diamond and ruby ring and Bessie had a sapphire and diamond. They both planned to hold their weddings in the little church of St Mary the Virgin. Bessie and Arthur would marry at the end of September 1914, Clara and Ernest in the October. They were so happy; life was good, the future looked bright and their sun was in the ascendant. But, of course, the storm clouds gathered. On 28th June 1914 Archduke Franz Ferdinand and his wife Sophie of Austria were assassinated in Sarajevo. Kaiser Wilhelm II of Germany offered support to Austria and marched on Serbia, Russia got rattled and, in August, Britain declared war on Germany. Thus began the general scrimmage which was the Great War!

"Don't worry, my darling," assured Ernest, kissing Clara goodbye. "It will all be over by Christmas. We can have a spring wedding instead."

"Keep your bottom drawer ready, old girl!" said Arthur to Bessie. "We shall have that wedding in May, you'll see."

The girls waved their handkerchiefs until the train chugged out of sight. They dried their eyes and put their wedding dreams on hold.

The first letters were mundane. They said the usual things - how much they missed them, keep the home fires burning, all that sort of nonsense. Then there was nothing for a week or more in October. One day, late in October, Bessie had a visit from Arthur's father. Without a word he handed her a black edged letter with an official stamp. It had been opened. It spoke of the death in battle of his beloved son, Arthur Sydney Fanshawe.

Mrs Baines sent for Clara. She could do little to ease the pain and wretchedness that her friend felt. She could just be there and hold her while she sobbed. Clara stayed at the Baines farmhouse with Bessie for several days until the rawness had passed, to be replaced by a dull ache. Bessie locked her bottom drawer and placed Arthur's picture safely into a gold locket – she still wore it in the days when I knew her - then carried on with day-to-day life. The girls knitted socks and scarves and sent them to the troops. They busied themselves helping out with the less fortunate and poorer local families who had also lost loved ones.

The following May Clara watched Bessie coming up her path with Mr Fanshawe, Ernest's father. They looked pale and serious, he was holding a letter with black edging. Clara's knees gave way and she swooned! Poor Ernest had fallen at the second battle of Ypres. There would be no wedding that year!

Two more tragedies blighted Clara's life during that terrible conflict. Her two older brothers were lost at Paschendale and in the battle of the Somme respectively.

In the closing months of the conflict Bessie also lost her only brother. After the armistice Bessie busied herself with the farm as her father seemed to have aged considerably since losing his only son

Clara needed a change of scenery. She was accepted as a seamstress at Hampton Court. This came with a grace and favour apartment. She was still able to travel to Sussex and see Bessie on days off and during holidays. Years passed, Clara's youngest brother married a girl from Norfolk and moved up to Sherringham. Her aged parents died and she inherited half of their estate. She still lived in her Hampton Court apartment, but now she stayed with Bessie on visits. After the death of Bessie's father, the farm passed to her youngest cousin; however, she had been catered for with the inheritance of a very large cottage, with an acre of garden. It was in this 'Baines Cottage' that Clara spent each holiday, plus many weekends and days off. One day in the late 1940's Bessie rang her in London.

"The large building plot next to the cottage is up for sale!" She told Clara, excitedly.

Clara was about to retire and needed a place to live. She purchased the land - about ¾ of an acre, and had a bungalow built on it surrounded by a large garden. She called it 'Fanshawes'.

She had retired there some 20 years previously and the two old friends had had several happy years. Each day they would meet in one or the other house and enjoy lunch together. They would shop together, garden together and reminisce about times long gone. Years passed and they aged. Clara developed severe arthritis and could hardly get around. Bessie was losing her sight and had suffered a mild stroke. This made her shaky on her legs. I went in to both ladies to administer their medicines and to give Bessie her eye drops. Not a visit passed without each lady asking fondly after the other and sending love to each other. Their contact was by telephone and, on most weeks, after church on Sundays, when WI volunteers helped them to the service and coffee afterwards. Such sad lives, I reflected. The war was a complete waste - not just for the fallen but for the lives those left behind might have had.

Both Bessie and Clara now lie in the churchyard at St Mary's.

'Fanshawes' passed to Clara's nephew from her brother, Arnold. Bessie's cousins' children still run the farm and rent out

Baines Cottage to a family with three children and a large dog. I still drive past the houses occasionally and think of the old friends, but always with a lump in my throat!

Sister under Scrutiny

I pulled into the farmyard at Mascalls Farm and swung around to the ugly little bungalow where Pat and Jed Beale lived. I parked my ancient Morris with a crunch of gravel. The Geese heard this and came waddling up to us honking a welcome. Pat Beale was an attractive 43 year old lady in the latter stages of a very aggressive disease. This had confined her to a wheelchair so that the farmer, Mr Mascall, had allowed the bungalow to be adapted with wheelchair ramps and lower kitchen fittings. Jed Beale was an excellent, loyal worker and, by all accounts, a brilliant stocksman held in high esteem by Mr Mascall. Rather than lose Jed, he had adjusted his hours to fit around caring for Pat. Jed had to leave the bungalow at 5.30am, so we went in at a more sociable hour to get Pat up and ready for the day. She would then cook a main meal for Jed's Break at 12 o clock. They spent until 3.30pm together and then he would go back to the farm. Soon after their evening supper, Jed would get Pat back to bed for the night.

Today I was accompanied by Mrs White. Once every year we district nurses would be observed on our rounds by the senior nurse manager. Today was my turn. Mrs White hadn't been with us very long I had only met her briefly on one occasion. I thought it prudent, therefore, to leave Pip, my scruffy mongrel, at home (much to his disgust). In the 1970s it was common practice for our dogs to travel with us in the car. It was company on the rural rides. We nurses were, at that time, using our own vehicles, and receiving minimal expenses which barely covered the cost of the petrol. Mrs White looked a little tense - eying the geese with some trepidation. "Don't mind them," I said, "they are as gentle as lambs. I've even fed them toast crumbs out of my hand." The moment the words left my lips the geese seemed to turn into murderous hissing, screeching banshees! Mr Mascall was driving round from the main farmhouse in his elderly Landrover and heading towards the main road. The geese chased him, furiously pecking at the retreating vehicle and hissing in a frightening manner. Once he was out of sight, they returned once again to the gentle, benign creatures of a few minutes previously - hopefully looking for the odd toast crumb. We knocked and went inside the bungalow. I introduced Mrs White to Pat and then did what I had to, making pleasant chit-chat all the while. As we were leaving and Pat was showing us to the door, we heard the screeching cacophony once again as the geese went mad. Sure enough we could hear Mr Mascall's Landrover returning. "What's all the row about?" I asked Pat. "Oh, those creatures hate Mr

108

Mascall!" She explained. "I don't understand." I replied. "He is very good to all his animals." "Oh I know," she said, "but he had that old Landrover laid up in the cart barn for months last winter. Those birds made it their home nesting underneath it for warmth and shelter. When he moved it, fixed it up and got it back on the road, they were furious with him for stealing their home! Now every time they see him they want to kill him! He'll just be back from the village with the morning papers." This amused us greatly, especially since, when we passed them on our way out, they were, once again, sweet, placid and gentle.

Our next visit was to particular favourites of mine. Jeremy and Phyllida Mole were a couple in their later years living in a very beautiful, substantial, stone-built house in a pretty village with their fat old black Labrador, Suzy. Jeremy, a retired barrister, had a leg ulcer which needed regular dressing. Philly needed weekly iron injections for her anaemia. Jeremy had recently retired from chambers in London. Now he was "cluttering up the place all day, under my feet" - as Philly affectionately put it. He was, usually, still at the breakfast table when we arrived, reading his Times and eking out the dregs of the coffee pot. The house smelt seductively of fresh coffee and toast (with a tiny bit of dog!) After mutual introductions, the routine began. I followed Philly upstairs to their bedroom and gave her the injection, then, after washing my hands in their en-suite, I would go downstairs, dress Jeremy's leg whilst Philly brewed fresh coffee to be taken by all of us in the elegant drawing room. Back in the 1970's most people smoked cigarettes. As a nurse I was not a regular smoker, but I did enjoy the odd one socially; and, twice a week, at the Mole's house, Philly would bring in a huge tray with fresh coffee, 2 rich tea biscuits for me to feed to Suzy, an ashtray and Jeremy's expensive Sobranie cigarettes with his gold lighter. There would then be a sociable twenty minutes together before I continued my rounds and Philly did the washing up. I had decided that I had better decline the cigarette today since Mrs White might not approve. We were, after all, supposed to be promoting health and wellbeing. Today Mrs White and I sat with Jeremy (and Suzy) in the drawing room. There was a large Inglenook fireplace and we expectantly awaited the coffee. Philly entered with the tray and much fuss was made of Suzy whilst we fed her rich tea biscuits. Philly poured the coffee. On cue, Jeremy offered the cigarettes. Before I could (politely) refuse, Mrs White had reached across me, taken one (with great thanks!), lit it, and taken a massive pull from it! She sat back, blowing smoke rings with a satisfied sigh. "Thanks for that!" she said "I was gasping for a fag!" A congenial fug of smoke filled the room as we all smoked and drank the excellent coffee.

Twenty minutes later we were back in the car and on the road again. "Isn't that Suzy a lovely dog?" she said. "I really miss my collie, Tiggy, today. She usually comes to work with me, but I thought it may not be fair on you in your car." I burst out laughing, "Oh I wish you had," I said, "She would have found a new friend with Pip, my mongrel. They would have got along just fine" and I'm getting along just as fine with Mrs White, I thought to myself.

Sister in Demand

I walked through the front door of the chalet bungalow to be greeted by a sobbing sixteen year old girl, who flung herself into my arms in great distress. Her eighteen year old sister had locked herself in the bathroom and was refusing to come out while Dad sat at the kitchen table staring at his hands and humming tunelessly.

This was the part of my job I hated; dealing with the patient's relatives at the end of a loved one's life. It was particularly hard when the patient was only forty two years old.

Penny and Malc lived in a pristine chalet bungalow on a new estate in the little Sussex market town where I was a district nurse. They had two lovely daughters and a little dog - everything to live for and a bright future, until Penny was diagnosed with terminal cancer. Her one wish was to die at home surrounded by her loved ones. This was the early '70's there and were very few hospice nurses available in the community, so us district nurses covered their care around the clock (along with their own loved ones, of course).

Penny was lucky in that her next door neighbour had also become her closest friend. Sylvie was a hairdresser who worked from home or visited her clients. She had become invaluable in nursing her friend, supporting the girls, cooking for Malc and keeping the house clean for them.

That weekend was particularly hard as my colleague had visited the previous evening to set up a syringe driver of morphine so that Penny's pain could be controlled. The doctor had arrived and had told Malc and the girls that it was unlikely Penny would survive the weekend and to prepare for the end. Her suffering would soon be over. It had been my weekend off and, in any case, I only worked mornings at that time. As luck would have it, out of five of us district nurses covering that area, three were off sick with various illnesses themselves. That week I and my colleague, Mary, had to cover a fairly widespread rural area and the market town. At the weekend, leaving my husband and young daughter with enough food and chores to keep them amused, I embarked on a full time, non- stop round of patient calls.

Penny needed visiting three times a day at that time. It was during my afternoon visit on the Saturday that Hannah, her youngest daughter, had broken down in my arms. Leading her through to the kitchen, I sat her down at the table and drew up a chair. I told them that it was imperative that the last few hours they spent with Penny were quality hours. Hard as it was, for her sake, they needed to be strong and to sit with her. She could still hear them even though the morphine was keeping her fairly sedated. Leaving Malc consoling Hannah, I headed for the bathroom to extricate the older girl.

Just as I was finishing my care for Penny, Sylvie gently tapped on the door and walked in. I was so impressed at her gentleness with her friend. She brushed and stroked her hair, and spoke to her - softly conjuring up visions of peaceful lakes with swans on, golden sunshine on the water and green trees. She told her that she could see verdant pastures and stone cottages with wisteria growing over their doors. I was fascinated. Penny was peaceful as I finished writing her notes and Sylvie and I left her with Hannah, holding her hand and whispering in her ear.

Sylvie had spent more time in Penny's house that last month than she had her own. Each day she washed her, helped to change the bed and kept her hair beautifully. She filed and painted her fingernails and had kept her company for hours when Malc had been working. Now, in her final few days, even though Penny might not have been aware, she was there for the whole family. "I know she may be able to hear me, Sister." She told me "So I conjure up these peaceful scenes for her. If she can dream of those, then she will be at peace when the end comes."

My colleague would be visiting in the evening, so I left them for the afternoon. Sylvie was sitting next to Malc at the kitchen table. She had a casserole in the oven for their dinner and her arm was around Malc's shoulders as he sobbed into his hands. Her dulcet tones were soothing him while the girls sat with Penny.

That was the last that I saw of them. Penny passed away during the night and Mary, my colleague, was working first thing in the morning on the following day so was there to support the newly bereaved family - along with their trusted friend and neighbour, Sylvie.

Some four months later I was coming out of the bank in the little town when I bumped into Sylvie. Her face lit up when she saw me and she gave me a hug. "Hello, Sister!" She greeted. In response to my enquiry after Malc and the girls, her face flushed. "I am living with them now." She told me: "My husband grew tired of me always being there; but what could I do, Sister? They needed me, the girls needed a mother figure and Malc needed me more than anyone. I had always loved him and Penny and it's what she would have wanted. We are getting married as soon as my decree absolute comes through!"

I was somewhat thoughtful as I drove away to my next patient. Did Sylvie nurse her friend out of love and neighbourly duty or had her motive been Malc all along? And did Malc really love her or was it a rebound reaction from a man who couldn't cope alone? I would never discover the truth of it and only time would tell, but I hoped that it had made Penny's passing easier and that she was now at peace.

To show the contrasts in my job; after I left Sylvie, I popped into the village shop to buy bread and milk and started chatting to Mr Paige, the shopkeeper. He looked over my shoulder out of the shop window and winked at me. "Here comes Mr Gissa! Now we shall have some fun, Sister! Watch this."

I turned to see a wrinkled thin man in his 60's walking towards the open shop doorway with a small black mongrel dog on a lead pulling him along for all it was worth. Mr Paige's shop was next to the village butcher's and this little dog seemed to be on a mission to get to the sausages. Apparently, the man would come to the open shop doorway to buy his wares as dogs were not allowed inside the shop. He stuck his head through the open shop door and, holding a £5 note out, exclaimed "Gissa!" before the dog dragged him out again. There was a repeated head through the door. "Gissa! Gissa! Wait! Damn dog! Gissa!" He was then pulled away again. Mr Paige, struggling to keep a serious face, raised one eyebrow. "What can I get for you Mr Forrest?" "Gissa! Gissa! Come here sodding animal!" And he disappeared towards next door before returning back again; "Gissa!" This went on for some time. Every time Mr Forrest got his head and hand with the money through the shop doorway, the little dog would pull him out towards the butcher's again, with much swearing and cussing from "Mr Gissa."

Finally with superhuman effort, he forced his shoulder through the doorway, held out the fiver. He managed: "Gissa nounse of golden and a packet of greens!" before disappearing for another twenty seconds. Mr Paige leisurely collected the tobacco and cigarette papers and strolled over to the shop door. As Mr Forrest reappeared (briefly) he thrust them into his hand with the change and grabbed the fiver before the dog pulled him away again. Mr Forrest's thanks were interspersed with "Wait! Damn dog!" and "stop pulling, ye bugger!" as he disappeared.

Grinning I turned to Mr Paige. "He has the same order every evening, Sister. I know what he wants, but it's far more entertaining to see him struggle with Pippin there. That's why we call him Mr Gissa."

I laughed: "Mr Paige, you are incorrigible."

I smiled as I left him to continue my rounds. It was just what I needed to cheer me up on such a day.

A Love for Beryl

"I'm delighted for you, Beryl" I really am!" I said, edging away from her. "I hope it all goes well and I wish you every good luck for the future. Must dash now; patients to see." I had popped into the local minimarket to pick up a loaf and some milk whilst on my rounds as a district nurse when I had bumped into Beryl Brown by the bacon counter. Beryl was the sister of one of my former patients, now deceased. She had been housekeeper and cook to her two older brothers and also nursed Ted (the youngest) for some five years following a major stroke which had left him bedridden before another massive stroke finally caused his demise.

I needed to get away from her that day as Beryl Brown could talk for England and I really did have to continue my patient rounds. This was the 1970's and we district nurses had large rural areas to cover in comparatively slow cars. Beryl herself was a little 'slow' and, therefore, tended to repeat herself several times, but I was genuinely happy for Beryl. Life had dealt her a rough hand and she deserved a little happiness in her final years. As I drove from the little town towards my next patient, I recalled what I knew of Beryl's life.

Her parents had been sheep farmers and had farmed several acres of downland. In those days farming was intense and harsh if a living was to be made. John, her eldest Brother, had been born and then, two years later, Mrs Brown delivered another boy who only lived for a few hours. Three years after that Ted had arrived. There had followed a series of miscarriages until, finally, ten years after John, Mrs Brown managed to safely deliver the longed-for daughter and Beryl was born. Mr Brown and the boys thought Beryl was their little princess and she was thoroughly spoilt by them. The Browns dressed her in frills and taught her all the skills needed by a countrywoman in the early 1930's. Beryl could cook and bake anything, skin and butcher game, gut fish and turn shirt collars; however, her intellect was limited following a tragic accident. When she was seven years old she fell from her father's tractor while riding with him. She had landed on the concrete yard - narrowly missing the wheels. She did, however, sustain a serious blow to the head. She was carried unconscious into the house and a doctor was sent for, but Beryl was comatose for several days. When she awoke - much to everyone's relief - it was apparent that she would live and her memory was intact. Unfortunately, following the accident, she was subject to seizures from time to time and her intellect was somewhat impaired. This made Mr Brown and the boys even more protective of her and she was rarely out of the sight of at least one of them. By the age of twelve she had concluded a sketchy education at the local school and then acted as deputy housekeeper (to her mother) in the family home.

When Beryl was in her early teens, Mr Brown died leaving twenty four year old John as the head of the household. Sheep farming was very hard and yielded but a poor living at that time. John was not very keen and Ted had no interest at all so it was decided to sell the farm. Property and land prices had risen steeply and there were some nice mock-Tudor houses being built on the edge of town so they purchased one of those. Ted could drive and had an eye for a bargain so he and John rented a lock-up shop in the town, purchased a lorry and started a house-clearance business together. Mrs Brown faded fast after the move so Beryl kept house and looked after them all. The boys were happy running the business and playing cricket for the local team, but Beryl felt trapped and frustrated with just the family for company. She spent her leisure hours reading since John would not allow a television in the house. She was particularly keen on a certain cheap series of paperback romance stories and, as she read these, she dreamed that maybe, one day, a handsome prince would come and whisk her away to care for her own castle.

It was not long before Mrs Brown passed away. John and Ted became even more protective towards Beryl. They didn't like her going out without one of them except, occasionally, to the local shops. Instead she read paperbacks and women's magazines, listened to the radio and dreamed. Sometimes she would see a poster in the town advertising a local dance or hop but when she asked her brothers if she could go, they agreed but insisted on accompanying her. They would only let her dance with them and any potential dance partners were soon scared off by the glares and glowers from the brothers.

Beryl soon got out of the habit of going anywhere on her own except for shopping in the town, where she would dream about buying pretty things for her own cottage and husband one day. She busied herself buying good quality food and cooking up more and more wonderful meals for the three of them from recipes she had heard on the radio or read in magazines. The years passed and the weight piled on poor Beryl until she resembled a small cottage loaf. She did, however, have a good complexion, clear blue eyes and fairish curly hair. At the age of fifty eight, Ted had his first major stroke. In the 1970's treatment was not very advanced for stroke victims. Ted decided that he enjoyed being an invalid and took to his bed, leaving John to run the business on his own. Poor Beryl had to nurse him - which is where I was called in. I visited daily and supported Beryl with his care and medication. John ran the shop, then sat in his chair all evening whilst Beryl toiled all day, cooked and washed up in the evening. Ted simply read back copies of Millers Antiques and slept most of the day. Two years later John decided to sell up the shop and retire; then Beryl had both brothers to run around after. She kept up her strength by eating even more!

When Ted was sixty three he developed a chest infection which necessitated a stay in hospital and it was there that a massive stroke claimed his life.

Once Beryl and John had recovered from the shock, life continued much in the same way, only now, with no Ted to nurse, Beryl had a little more time to herself, more time to read her romantic novels and to dream. John found that he missed having male company and, while he no longer played cricket, he was still a member of the local club. He took to visiting the clubhouse every Friday evening where he propped up the bar with an old, recently widowed pal. David Simkins was five years younger than John but they got on well and, eventually, became good friends. One evening John invited David to dinner the following Friday. Such an invitation would have been unheard of when Ted was alive. Beryl duly cooked up a sumptuous meal of prawn cocktail, beef stew with dumplings and a bramley apple crumble with custard to finish. David had brought some brown ale for himself and John and a bottle of Liebfraumilch for Beryl. She had put on her best dress and had found the compact of face powder and lipstick which she had hidden in her drawer - bought many years previously and last worn at Ted's funeral. The food was delicious, the wine went to Beryl's head and the evening was such a success that David suggested that he bought them all a takeaway Chinese meal the following Friday. Beryl had never eaten Chinese food before and found that she absolutely loved it. To her this was the height of sophistication. Thus a regular pattern evolved. One week Beryl would cook something delicious, the next David would bring a different meal from the local Chinese takeaway's menu. Beryl lived for those evenings. She bought more face powder and different coloured lipstick and sent for new clothes from the mail order catalogue (without telling John).

Two years after Ted's death David was invited to spend Christmas with them. They agreed that he should stay over to Boxing day in Ted's old room so that he could have a few drinks without having to drive his Morris Minor back to his small flat. It was a wonderful Christmas day. Beryl's turkey dinner and plum pudding was a masterpiece and John even allowed Beryl to dance with David to the Christmas music on their old radiogram. They retired to bed replete and happy a little before midnight.

On Boxing morning Beryl got up and made breakfast. John seemed to be sleeping late so she took a cup of tea up to his room. David heard a crash and a tinkle of crockery coupled with a stifled cry.

Taking the stairs two at a time, he found Beryl in the doorway with her hand over her mouth. The teacup was smashed on the floor. John was leaning half out of bed. His face was navy blue. He was stone cold dead. He had, apparently, suffered a massive heart attack.

David took charge. He was a tower of strength to Beryl. He knew her learning difficulties meant that she would be unable to manage her finances and insurance policies, or to organise a funeral. She had been left comfortably off and, although the house had not been decorated or modernised in thirty years, it was, nonetheless, worth a small fortune. David was only sixty and Beryl a mere fifty five. Six months after John's untimely death David asked Beryl to marry him.

It was that happy news that she had imparted to me that morning in the local shop. "Are you having a registry office wedding?" I asked. "Oh! No sister!"

She sounded shocked. "I am going to have a white wedding in St Nicholas' with a princess dress, a long train and a veil. David has two teenage nieces and they will be my bridesmaids, just like in the books." She looked blissfully happy and almost attractive. It may have taken her fifty five years, I thought, but Beryl had found her Prince Charming at last.

Sister on the rounds

I sat in my car shaking for a few minutes. I was so angry, gossip could be so cruel and Mrs Beaufort didn't need that now. Not on top of all her problems.

Mr and Mrs Beaufort lived in a rather large detached Victorian house on the outskirts of a salubrious village. Their son, Timothy, was twenty one years old and in the final stages of terminal bowel cancer. Their younger daughter was away at university and the Beaufort's had turned their dining room into a downstairs bedroom for Timothy so that he could be cared for at home in his final days. From there he could see the lovely garden through the French doors.

I usually visited him twice a day to give him his painkilling medication and to support the family. Mrs Beaufort was an attractive woman in her early forties. Slim with dark hair, she had been an artist. Her musician husband travelled up to London most evenings to play professionally in his orchestra.

People cope with grief in different ways. Mrs Beaufort kept herself constantly busy with Timothy's care but, on the few occasions when I saw Mr Beaufort, he was shut away in his study-cum-studio playing his piano intently as if he were in a trance.

Dr Jenkins, the local GP, was a very kind and conscientious man. He was an old fashioned doctor who really cared for his patients as people. Nothing was too much trouble for him and he was a pillar of strength to Mrs Beaufort. She lived just a short distance from the surgery so he popped in most days to see Timothy and his parents.

That day I had just come from our weekly staff meeting. The evening district nurse had caught me after the meeting and asked me outright if it were true that Dr Jenkins was having an affair with Mrs Beaufort! It seemed that she had seen him giving her a hug on her doorstep as she drove past the house one evening and she had heard that his car was often seen in the Beaufort's drive. Didn't Mr Beaufort work evenings In London? (There was much in the same vein).

I was furious! Dr Jenkins popped in most evenings after surgery to settle Timothy for the night with his controlled pain killing drugs. Being a kind man, when Mrs Beaufort was in tears, he would hug her - the way most compassionate human beings would. To hear of this being twisted into something that sounded so sordid was not only unfair but it made me angry too.

I rarely lost my temper in those days, but this riled me so much that I flew at the evening nurse telling her how slanderous it was and assuring her that if the Beaufort's or Dr Jenkins heard about it, no doubt prosecutions for slander would follow. I finished by telling her to scotch all rumours of this at once or face the consequences. I then swept out of the room and into my car. I drove furiously to the nearest lay by where I pulled over to calm myself down.

What sort of world was it where someone could not offer basic comfort and compassion to another human without starting lewd speculation and rumour!

Timothy died a few days later, and before his twenty second birthday. Mr and Mrs Beaufort sold up and moved nearer to London so as to be handy for his work and nearer to their daughter, who had decided to stay on at her University college and take her Master's degree. Dr Jenkins continued to be a wonderful, caring and conscientious Doctor to his patients.

Sometimes the pain of bereavement is too much to bear, as was the case in the story of Elsie. Elsie lived with her ageing parents in a smart Georgian town house close by the church in the little market town. She had been a primary school teacher but had retired at fifty to care for her parents, who were becoming dependant.

Her father had developed Parkinson's disease and suffered the dementia that, sadly, often accompanies it. Elsie brought her mother to see him in the care home every day. In his final hours Elsie sat by his bed kissing his hands and talking to him constantly.

When death released him from his suffering, she threw all her energies into caring for her mother who was in her eighties. She had suffered heart problems since her mid-seventies. In the latter months she couldn't walk more than a few paces without needing oxygen. Elsie was marvellous. She spent her days and nights caring for her mother's every need.

We visited, of course, to offer support and to supervise the medication, but Elsie did all the main caring herself. In the last few weeks of her life Mrs Deacon was bedridden and barely sensible. Elsie sat with her every day holding her hands, kissing her and telling her how much she loved her. She always called her 'mummy' and we all feared for Elsie's health when 'mummy' finally passed away.

Inevitably this happened. One day, we arrived to find Elsie in tears holding her mother to her and still talking to her. With gentle hands we parted her so that Turner the undertaker could take the body. With gentle voices we comforted Elsie as much as we could but she had no other relatives and we couldn't seem to assuage her grief.

We were so concerned for Elsie, that we started calling in on her every day to support her. We tried to get her involved in the church choir, the flower club, the WI, then amateur dramatics but nothing would tempt her from the house.

She busied herself during the first few days working on the funeral arrangements. Some of my colleagues went to see Mrs Deacon laid to rest with her husband in the churchyard across the road from the house they had lived in. Elsie handled herself very well during the service.

Mrs Jeffrey, the vicar's wife, had helped her prepare a light spread back at the house, and a few of the parishioners went back there after the service to pay their last respects.

We all expected life to settle down for Elsie but one day we heard some shocking news. The postman had called but, as he put the letters through the letterbox, he noticed that the previous day's mail was still on the mat and the milk still on the doorstep. He knocked and then rang the doorbell. When he could get no reply he went to the local police station.

They found Elsie in the bath. She had run a bath full of water, climbed in (fully clothed) and opened her wrists with one of her father's old razor blades. She was dead and cold.

We all felt a great sympathy for Elsie, but none of us could think of anything else that would have made a difference to her. She had lived her life for her parents and couldn't live without them. Sometimes life can be so sad.

People can be very strange. Most of my patients were extremely generous. At Christmas we district nurses had lunch paid for by a trust set up by one of our grateful patients. We received gifts of vegetables, chocolates and eggs. But on occasions we could be taken for granted.

Mr Desmond was a man who needed dressings to his leg ulcers twice weekly. He lived in a big house too far from the cottage hospital to attend the out patients clinic for these, so we went into his house to do them. Or rather I did. My colleagues refused to attend him. The problem was that Mr Desmond had six large, hairy German Shepherd dogs that he refused to tether or keep locked away when we visited. I am a dog lover, but even I felt a little concerned the first time I called on him. I rang the bell and a cacophony of barking and yelping broke out. Through the glass in his front door I could see what looked like fifty wolves baying and charging down the hallway towards the door. I thought he would call them back or lock them in the front room, but no. He opened the door shouting to me above the din that if I stood my ground they wouldn't hurt me.

He was absolutely right. I stood still and avoided eye contact with them. Once they realised I wasn't afraid they let me pat them and stroke them. Many a pair of my tights was ruined by their big paws, which they would lift up and drag down my legs when vying for my attention. Whilst I loved dogs, even I found it all a bit much to cope with. My less enthusiastic colleagues would have none of it at all and so his dressings were down to me. Our senior Nursing officer was all for withdrawing his treatment unless he agreed to keep the dogs locked up, but I felt sorry for him. He loved his dogs and he had a lonely existence. I could manage them so it was agreed, after I had intervened on his behalf, that I would visit him twice a week.

I arrived one day and Mr Desmond greeted me with his camera. "Sister, would you mind if I got a picture of you with the boys please?" he asked. "Not at all" I replied and posed with all six of his dogs while he happily snapped away.

About two weeks later I had finished his dressings. He hobbled to his dresser in the sitting room and pulled out an envelope with photos in. "Look, Sister, I have them back from the developers." He showed me the pictures of me posing with the dogs and I made appropriate noises of approval. "This is a particularly nice one of you with Prince, Sister, would you like to keep it?"

I wasn't really fussed but he seemed so keen that I tried to sound enthusiastic "Oh yes! Why, thank you Mr Desmond!" as I took the print. "You're welcome, Sister." he replied, then, holding out his hand: "That will be sixty pence!"

The new community hospital housed all clinical services under one roof, but, before it was built, things had been very different. I, and the other district nurses, had our office and supplies in a clinic building attached to the local library and next door to the sorting office. It had a separate entrance and we shared it with the health visitors, midwives and physiotherapists. It was only manned during clinic hours, so we all had our own individual keys.

On that particular day it was hot - extremely hot. I had started out wearing my navy blazer, which was part of our summer uniform, but had become so overheated in my car – remember that this was the days before air conditioning was common - that I had shed my blazer onto the back seat and continued in my short sleeved dress.

I had to pop into the clinic to pick up some more dressing supplies. I was in a hurry and the door was open so I rushed in. There was a rather slow, round and bad tempered health visitor called Mavis. She was in the clinic when I arrived, clearing up after the anti- natal group. I called hello but, as ever, was ignored. I was physically in the supplies cupboard when I heard her slam the door as she left the building. Typical, I thought. Mostly we would call "goodbye" or some remark, but not her.

133

I collected all the supplies I needed and made my way out. However, she had locked the door behind her. With a sense of growing horror I realised that my keys were in my blazer pocket on the back seat of my car!

What to do? I could ring the hospital and hope that someone would come and let me out. I could wait - hopefully someone would be in for the afternoon clinics - but I was rather busy and I needed to pick up my daughter from her nursery school within the hour. There was a big sash window and we were on the ground floor – salvation! I slid the window up. It wasn't really very high, and I was quite fit in those days. I dropped my big black nursing bag through, with all of my new supplies in, then gently threw my navy pill box hat after it.

Hitching up my skirts to an indecent height above my thighs I stepped onto the ledge, ducked under the window pane and jumped down. I turned and shut the window behind me and as I turned back to retrieve my hat and my bag I noticed him. A gangly, spotty post boy was watching me with open mouth and eyes as big as saucers. I had no choice but to bluff it out. Pulling my skirt down and cramming my ridiculous pill box hat on my head I turned and faced him: "Well?" I demanded. He gulped and fled! With as much dignity as I could muster I strode out to my car and onto my last patient of the morning.

For a few months I covered a colleague's maternity leave. This involved the twilight shift from 7pm until midnight. We always had an auxiliary nurse with us since it was safer to travel in twos at night. On this particular evening we received an emergency call-out to an elderly lady in a forest village some seven or eight miles from the market town.

This poor old lady was in the last stages of alcoholic liver failure. She was semi-comatose and the county hospital couldn't take her until the following day. We were instructed to visit and to ensure that she was comfortable for the night. The day staff would go in the morning and see her into the ambulance to the hospital.

Her dwelling was a very old cottage overlooking the churchyard in a particularly lonely part of the village. It was dark but we could clearly see the graves by the light of the moon. That evening was misty and the vapour over the graves gave an eerie gothic-like atmosphere. We had been instructed to let ourselves in by means of the key, which was hanging on a string through the letterbox. That was a common way for us to gain entry in those days. The house was deathly quiet. We knew the old lady was in an upstairs bedroom but what we hadn't bargained for was the fact that there were no lightbulbs in any of the downstairs light fittings. Using my small pen torch we crept through the sitting room to the stairs calling out reassuring words, more for our benefit than our patient's. Pat, my assistant, tried to hide behind me as I groped my way through the house. We noticed a huge empty inglenook fireplace which would have dominated the small sitting room had there been any furniture in it. I was told later that it had all been sold to fund our lady's addiction.

We groped our way upstairs by the rather inadequate torchlight. At the top of the stairs I was vaguely aware of a black shape on the floor, but not before I had tripped over it. "Yeeeeooooowwwww!" It rose up with a screech like a banshee, and fled downstairs. I had nearly landed on my face and Pat, who was holding onto my waist, almost landed on top of me. "What the f..." She tried to say but I was clutching my chest, convinced that my heart had stopped. Then the realisation dawned on us. It was a cat. A black cat; and we had fallen over it in the dark!

Luckily our poor patient was unaware of it, and unaware of us too I do believe. I found out later that her neighbour had taken the poor creature in when its mistress made her final journey to hospital. The cottage reverted to the Crown on her demise. That case stays in my mind and serves as proof that sorrow, fear and laughter are often very close companions. We nurses saw more than our fair share of all of those

Sister in Adversity

It was a typical shift in the 1970's during my working week. As a district nurse, I felt very lucky to be doing my work in such wonderful places. The downs had their own wild beauty – undulating but with a perishing cold wind at times. There were pretty, peaceful villages, small country towns, plenty of sheep and wild birds and hospitable, interesting people.

After leaving my patient, I took the road to Bucklebury and pulled over into one of my favourite quiet spots for coffee. I got out of the car and perched on the edge of the bonnet. As I unscrewed the lid of my flask the sparrows came plopping down beside me to see what goodies I might have. There were groups of starlings browsing amongst them. I saw the blue sky with the panoramic view of the countryside before me. The coffee was good and the only sound was of the gentle breeze and birdsong. England was the best place in the world and I felt wonderfully at peace and in love with the universe.

Soon I was brought back to earth! After I had left my patient in Bucklebury, I had stopped at the village shop to pick up a daily paper and some milk halfway through my round. I turned the key in the ignition – click click! Nothing else. "Damn! Not again!" I thought to myself: "I must get this to a garage soon!" It was the third time that particular week that this had happened to me. My ancient Morris had a battery fitted with 'pop-off' terminals - an ironic name for them as mine seemed to 'pop-off' just whenever they felt like it, and usually at the most inconvenient times. (Thankfully the modern cars don't have such things.)

As I came out of the shop my uniform had attracted the attention of a van load of workman who had parked next to me to enjoy their flasks of coffee and hot pies freshly purchased from the shop. They wolf whistled and the balding driver called out: "Morning Sister, I don't feel too good", His colleagues giggled as though this was the height of wit. I pointedly ignored them, this was an occupational hazard which nurses in uniform faced at that time. My cool was soon blown however, when my car refused to start!

"Wan' an 'and, darlin'?" Enquired the balding one, with a silly grin on his face. "I'm fine, thank you!" I snapped, stiffly. Being used to this problem and, finding myself not strong enough to press the terminals back tightly enough, I had taken to carrying a hide mallet with me. It was resting behind the driver's seat in my car ready for just such an occasion as this. I popped the bonnet and checked the terminals – The men nudged each other and smirked; from their position they couldn't see under the bonnet at all. I strolled nonchalantly to my car and produced the hide mallet. This produced peals of raucous laughter and some inane comments from the men. "Mind ya temper now, Sister!" called Baldy. I hit each terminal in turn with the mallet. RAP RAP! Dropping the bonnet and tossing the mallet back into the car, I thought they would explode into hysterics; but instead they turned to amazed gasps as the engine sprang to life. I drove off with a wave and a toot. Their faces were a picture that stays with me to this day.

I had left my visit to Mrs Day until last on that particular day. She and her husband Ray ran the beef farm next door to my own cottage and I usually stayed and had a coffee with her after I had finished her treatment. Dorry Day was recovering from surgery to remove a nasty lump from her breast; not an easy thing, especially when you are seventy years old. I called in every morning to change her dressing on my way home. Dorry was putting the kettle on while I washed my hands in her downstairs cloakroom by the front door when there was a knock at said door. "I'll get it." I called to her, as I was nearest. I was still drying my hands when I opened it to reveal the same van load of men that I had so recently entertained. They were parked in the lane outside the farm house. Baldy stood there looking awkward and a little embarrassed to see me; "Sister," he said sheepishly "your cow's loose in the lane." "Oh! Thanks. I replied, "It's not my cow, but I know where it's from – Dorry, one of Rays cows has busted out!" When they saw Mrs Day, the men decided that we feeble women were not up to the job and that they would take command. The others had jumped out of the van, sensing adventure, and two of them had managed to get past the poor frightened beast in the lane. Dorry and I rushed out of her drive to see the smallish Hereford hesitating as to which way to run. "You head her up our drive, Sister, and I'll open the gate to our side paddock. She'll be safe there until Ray gets back." said Dorry. The two intrepid hunters had driven her back towards me, I blocked the lane with my arms spread wide to usher her into the Day's drive, she had nowhere else to go, so she ran in panic up the drive followed by the whooping men who were by now, thoroughly enjoying themselves with cries of "Yee haw!" and "Tarnation, durn critter!" I could only see their backs when, suddenly, they all turned around abruptly and came running down the drive at breakneck speed. All mirth and smirks had disappeared and had been replaced by looks of sheer terror. Without a word they rushed past me, jumped into their van and screeched off before the van doors were even fully closed. Disgusted with them, I stood my ground, blocking the bottom of

140

the drive, arms spread wide to stop the beast. At the last second, I realised that the beast was not stopping. I sprang back as she charged past me just a whisker away. I felt the rush of air as it spun me round so that I saw her rear end disappearing down the drive. Except that it wasn't a her! Swinging between the beast's legs were the reason for the men's sudden retreat. She was a he! They had just been chased by a bull! Gentle coaxing and a bucket of cow cake eventually enticed him into the Day's side paddock and Dorry swung the gate shut behind him. "Phew!" she said "Now how about that coffee, Sister; Bells or Glenfiddich?"

When I visited her the next day she looked amused- "You know that young stirk we caught yesterday, Sister?" "Yes," I replied, "Did Ray find out which fence he had broken?" "Yes he found a fence post down right enough but, the point is, it wasn't one of his stirks at all!" She continued: "It had come from the Northfield area, two miles away. Luckily Ray knew the farm so, after our dinner, he trailered him back to his rightful owner." We smiled at each other, then suddenly the funny side struck us, and we giggled about it together all through coffee.

Sister in Practice

I spent a pleasant two years as a part time Practice nurse before going back to University and specialising. Glade Farm Surgery was a smallish three doctor practice in the small market town and I job-shared with my colleague, Agnes Simpson, each of us working two full days per week and together on a Thursday morning. Surgery closed half day on Thursdays.

I specialised in assisting with the minor operations, wart removal and cysts, while she did the baby immunisation clinics. However, we took over each other's role for holiday cover and sickness.

We had some colourful local characters frequenting the surgery and a few walking wounded through the doors. One in particular sticks in my mind. Pete worked at the local factory. He was about six feet five inches tall and very stocky. He had fair hair and a square shaped head, putting Agnes and myself in mind of Mary Shelley's monster from the Frankenstein novel. He was a man of very few words - which was fortunate as he had a very rough voice and was none too bright! To be perfectly honest, he scared us more than a little since he was quite unsmiling.

I had given him a tetanus injection when he was bitten by a dog once and Agnes had removed a large metal splinter from his hand, but that had been the limit of our dealings with him.

On the outskirts of the town was a large traveller camp. Generally speaking, we were seen as their friends since we helped the women to obtain free milk for their babies, assisted with contraception and letter writing to the local schools and all manner of other things.

I got on particularly well with a mother and daughter from the camp called Catt. Alice and Tabitha Catt thought I was the best thing since sliced bread because I was able to get them free nit lotion and baby milk. I loved the fact that they called each other "Tabby" and "Ali" especially in view of their surname. Not all of the travellers were so pleasant and funny though.

One day I was having my lunch in my room when the receptionist rang through to tell me a man had brought a child in with an injured hand.

"Show him into the treatment room, I'll be along directly." I told her and, shelving my tuna sandwich, I went down the corridor to meet them. My heart sank when I saw Joby King. Mrs King had been in frequently to have cuts and bruises treated, always alone and always begging us not to tell Joby that she had been to us. We knew he beat her, but, without her permission to act for her, we were helpless. Today he had his nine year old son Ben with him. Ben's face was tear-stained and his right hand and wrist were red and swollen with his thumb sticking out at an odd angle.

"What happened?" I asked It appeared that Ben had fallen upstairs in school in the rush to get to class. He had put out his hand to save himself and landed on it, wrenching his thumb in the process. School had sent for Mrs King who had wanted to take him to hospital, but Joby insisted that he just needed a bandage and should be fine. I went to examine Ben and he squealed in pain. From the angle of the thumb I suspected a dislocation at least, if not a fracture. "Man up, boy!" said Joby, gruffly, to his son "Let sister put a bandage on it then we can all get off home." I sighed "I'm afraid I can't do that, Mr King." I told him. "Ben needs to go to the hospital for an x-ray, it's either a fracture or a dislocation." He looked thunderous. "What nonsense! Just strap it up and let's be done with it." I stood my ground. "Sorry, but he needs to go...." I broke off as he stepped towards me looking menacing. Looming over me he poked me painfully on my right shoulder, while clenching his left fist. His face was thrust an inch away from mine. Ben burst into tears and covered his ears, "No, no dad! Don't! Please don't!" he sobbed. I knew he had witnessed his mum get the worst of Joby's temper before now. My knees turned to water and my stomach churned. I cursed my stupidity in letting him get between me and the door, and made a mental note to get the panic button moved from next to the door onto my side of the room. Standing to my full five feet four inches and thrusting out my chin I stood firm and said: "Let me get the doctor to see him first, then, please." He stepped back. "Now!" He demanded. I nodded and made a grab for the door handle. Once through I rushed into reception.

"Who's back from lunch?" I gasped; apparently I looked as white as a ghost. "Dr Gupta has just come back." replied Meg, the senior receptionist. Oh no, I thought. Of all the possible partners Dr Gupta was the smallest. He was a mild mannered, gentle man of about five feet six inches. Oh well! I concluded, he would have to do. I knocked on his door and entered. He listened to my story and his face changed into one of outrage. "How dare he treat my nurse like that?" he retorted. "Sister, you go back to your office and finish lunch. Leave this to me." And he strode into the treatment room with a determined air, whilst Meg and I listened with some dread and alarm outside the door. We fully expected to have to call the police, and possibly an ambulance for Dr Gupta. We could only hear muffled voices and then Dr Gupta came out.

"Meg! Please can you call a taxi to take Ben and Mr King to the county hospital." Joby looked sullen and moody but went quietly enough when the taxi arrived. I discovered later that it was just as I had suspected. Poor little Ben needed surgery on his hand.

"What Happened? What did you say to him?" We asked Dr Gupta. "Well it was all very simple!" he replied. "I told him that if he didn't get the child to a hospital immediately, I would report the campsite to social services and to the police!" We knew that Joby King would be most unpopular with the rest of the travellers if any official body, let alone the police, were to go sniffing around their encampment. Joby must have decided that hospital was preferable to incurring the wrath of his fellow travellers. A smart move by Dr Gupta!

As I went to go back to my office I saw Pete in the corner of the waiting room. "What's the trouble, Pete?" I questioned, motioning him into the treatment room. He held up his hand which was wrapped in a handkerchief, none too clean, and covered in blood. He chuckled: "I 'ad a row wiv the drill and I lorst!" He was grinning foolishly. I took a look. He had caught his index finger in the mechanical drill and had laid open a gash the entire length of it. A clean up, a few suture strips and then I was able to dress it for him. As I worked he asked: "What was all that about wiv that cocky sod, Sister?" I told him how Mr King had been threatening to me and how Dr Gupta had intervened. To my surprise Pete got quite animated. "If I 'ad known that I would 'ave punched 'is lights out, Sister! I won't 'ave anyone harm you or Sister Agnes! You two are angels and I won't 'ave that jumped up little bastard threaten you!" I knew he meant it. He continued: "Want me to go and sort 'im for you, Sister?" I assured him that that would not be necessary and thanked him for his concern. Sometimes my patients really surprised me!

Another patient who was a fan of ours was Mrs Langton. In particular she was a fan of Dr Page - or more like obsessed with Dr Page! Mrs Langton was in her late seventies and had suffered a small stroke in the past. She had high blood pressure but otherwise just needed her six monthly health check to keep her on track.

Dr Page was in his mid-thirties, happily married and with two children. The problem was that Mrs Langton failed to see why her feminine wiles would not tempt Dr Page away from his family. She showered him with gifts despite being asked not to. She constantly professed her love for him.

To maintain an ethical relationship, Dr Page had transferred Mrs Langton onto Dr Gupta's list, but she simply refused to attend surgery on Dr Gupta's days; turning up instead on Dr Page's days.

This went on for the best part of eighteen months. Mrs Langton was in the surgery every week with one imagined condition or another. She was quite the model hypochondriac. She would regularly phone the surgery asking to speak to Dr Page, sometimes several times a week. Despite Dr Page returning gifts and begging her to desist, he regularly received love letters from her and photographs of Mrs Langton dressed in anything from her lacy housecoat to full evening dress.

One day the junior partner, Dr Watson, was called out to Mrs Langton's bungalow by her cleaner. The lady had turned up to do her work only to find Mrs Langton dead. She had suffered another stroke, but a massive and fatal one this time.

Dr Watson signed her death certificate, the undertakers came and, in due course, she was buried in the local churchyard.

About a month after Mrs Langton's funeral, the surgery was experiencing an extremely hectic time. A flu epidemic had hit the town and the phone was ringing non-stop with requests for home visits.

Dr Page came into the staff room to grab a coffee after morning surgery one day. He was looking somewhat harassed. "You look like a busy man!" Meg said to him. "Yes" he replied "I just got a request to visit Mrs Langton." I looked up quickly but Meg gasped: "B-b-b but she died! She's lying in St Gregory's buried six feet under!" "Yes, I know!" Explained Dr Page. "Now she thinks she's got worms!" He winked at me as he left, stealing the biscuit from my hand!